Creating Product Value

Putting Manufacturing on the Strategic Agenda

Creating
Product Value

Putting Manufacturing on
the Strategic Agenda

ARNOUD De MEYER
in collaboration with
AVIVAH WITTENBERG-COX

FINANCIAL TIMES

PITMAN PUBLISHING

Pitman Publishing
128 Long Acre, London WC2E 9AN

A Division of Longman Group UK Limited

First published in 1992

© Arnoud De Meyer, 1992

A CIP catalogue record for this book can be obtained from the British
Library.

ISBN 0 273 60022 2

Phototypeset in Linotron Times Roman
by Northern Phototypesetting Co. Ltd., Bolton
Printed and bound in Great Britain

CONTENTS

I INTRODUCTION

Why a book about manufacturing strategy aimed at general managers? Because manufacturing remains an important element of a company's activities. General managers need to understand the challenges posed by manufacturing and contribute to formulating medium and long term manufacturing strategies. This book provides tools to analyse the changing role of manufacturing and to implement change.

MANUFACTURING STILL MATTERS

Some may think that manufacturing is a challenge of the past. Its role in economic activity seems to have declined and become largely peripheral. The future is proclaimed to lie with creating and selling services. The former UK Prime Minister's plan was to propel the country into the 21st century by turning it into a service-based economy. Manufacturing has retained the smell of the smoke-stack, along with its reputation for obsolete labour relations.

But these arguments are deceptive. In some respects, it is true that manufacturing is in decline. But Table 1.1 presents a more nuanced – and more accurate – picture. It presents data for two national European economies. The UK economy reveals a manufacturing component which has stabilised – if not declined. Germany's economy, on the other hand, built its post-war strength on strong manufacturing. For both countries, four figures are given:

Year	United Kingdom				Germany			
	Output index (1985=100)	Number of employees	Annual hours worked	Output per hour index (1985=100)	Output index (1985=100)	Number of employees	Annual hours worked	Output per hour index (1985=100)
1968	96.1	8189	1965	55.8	67.9	8851	1914	53.8
1970	100.0	8347	1911	58.6	79.9	9527	1905	59.0
1975	101.6	7510	1773	71.3	83.6	8655	1750	74.5
1980	96.8	6937	1695	76.9	96.3	8676	1719	86.8
1985	100.0	5362	1742	100.0	100.0	8061	1667	100.0
1990	118.3	5151	1754	122.3	112.9	8562	1619	109.4

Source: National Institute Economic Review 1992

Table 1.1   Selected data about manufacturing in Germany and the UK

- the total number of people employed in manufacturing industries
- the average number of hours worked per year
- the output per worker (1985 as a base year) and
- the total output of manufacturing industries (1985 base).

Enormous changes can be observed. In the UK, between 1968 and 1990, the number of people employed in the manufacturing sector dropped 37 per cent, while the number of hours worked decreased by 11 per cent. Total labour-based capacity in 1990 decreased 56 per cent compared to 1968. The German numbers are far less dramatic. Employment in manufacturing industries stagnated over the same period, total number of hours worked dropped by 15 per cent and labour-based capacity theoretically decreased 18 per cent.

For people primarily concerned with manufacturing's impact on employment, the picture is clear. But while employment was decreasing, manufacturing was making huge strides in productivity, through capital investment and improved production methods. Labour and total factor productivities increased so much that they have largely compensated for employment reductions (Table 1.2). Over the 1968 – 1990 period, manufacturing output actually grew at the same rate as the general economy.

This productivity growth was not limited to the 1960s or 1970s. Table 1.3 presents productivity gains over the 1983 to 1987 period for the US, Japan and four European countries. This data needs cautious interpretation as it reflects countries with very different

	Labour productivity (per worked hour)	Total factor productivity
UK	3.57	2.60
Germany	3.23	2.45

Source: National Institute Economic Review, 1992

Table 1.2 Average productivity growth from 1968–1979 (in %)

	Business Sector		Manufacturing Industry	
	Total factor productivity	Labour productivity	Total factor productivity	Labour productivity
United States	1.5	1.4	5.1	5.4
Japan	2.0	2.9	2.9	5.3
Italy	1.6	2.1	3.3	4.8
France	1.6	2.6	0.0	1.7
Germany	2.0	2.5	1.7	2.4
United Kingdom	1.8	1.9	3.5	3.9

Source: Based on OECD statistics

Table 1.3 Average annual total factor and labour productivity growth for the period 1983–1987

economic and political environments. Japan, at the time, was at the height of its economic growth, while France was recovering from a failed economic experiment carried out in the early 1980s. Although productivity growth fluctuated greatly from one country to another, the table shows that productivity generally grew faster in manufacturing than in other sectors. With the possible exception of France, labour productivity improved tremendously.

The picture that emerges is one of manufacturing as a more or less stable component of the economies of the industrialised world. Less people work less hours per year in manufacturing, but their output has grown enormously. Table 1.1 shows how output per hour worked has more than doubled in both the UK and Germany over a 22 year period. Macroeconomically, manufacturing industries still matter.

Widespread impact

But macroeconomic analyses limited to manufacturing industry statistics underestimate the true economic impact of manufacturing activities. Many services owe their existence to manufacturing. Just as agricultural and food processing industries exist in countries with a lot of farming, a strong and competitive manufacturing industry is needed to create a healthy service sector. Services are often intimately linked to manufacturing, as suppliers or as a result of manufacturing activities.

Many software developers thrive on creating software for use in process control or materials management. Dealers and after-sales car services would not exist if no Renaults or Toyotas were produced. In five years, television sets may be as much as 50 per cent software, and software development may become a key success factor in consumer electronics. But software fulfils its function only once hardware has been produced. This is not to suggest that manufacturing leads the rest of the economy. Not all services depend on manufacturing. Financial or travel services, for example, could exist without the manufacturing sector. But an economy's strength is based on the integration between the manufacturing sector and the agricultural and service sectors.

If abstraction is made of services independent of manufacturing (finance, insurance or leisure), Cohen and Zysman[1] argue that about 25 per cent of US GNP originates in services used as inputs by goods-producing industries. This is more than the manufacturing sector's contribution to GNP. Establishing the relationship between manufacturing and services created by manufacturing would dramatically change the proportional impact of manufacturing on the American economy. Manufacturing employment would no longer be described, as it often is in conventional economic studies, as something that, in 1953, employed one third of the American workforce but that has declined to only one-fifth today and is doomed to continue its fall.

Instead, the link between a broad range of services and manufacturing would be recognised. The total network of manufacturing activities, including upstream and downstream services, would employ 40 to 60 million American citizens. Half, or perhaps even three quarters of those routinely counted as service workers actually depend on manufacturing. Neglecting manufacturing and gradually shifting away from it could lead to a situation where economies simultaneously shift out of services like product or

---

[1] Cohen S. S. and Zysman J., 1987, *Manufacturing Matters*, Basic Books, New York.

process engineering, leaving only low-tech, low value-added service activities.

High-tech development support

Manufacturing is often perceived somewhat negatively, complete with smoke-stacks, smelly effluents, dangerous environmental impacts, and unpleasant working conditions. It is contrasted to the clean and attractive activities of the high-tech sector, such as genetic engineering, software development or materials services. But many high-tech industries are part of networks of traditional industries on which they depend for their development. The high-tech sector's R & D labs are closely tied to a strong manufacturing base. Most high-tech products are industrial goods, sold to industrial companies.

Successful high-tech industries must be able to live in symbiosis with their customers. Who else is going to tell high-tech companies what is really needed, how specifications for products should evolve, and what kind of trends can be expected in the future? Who will buy silicon chips and superconductive materials if producers of automobiles, machine tools, telephones, toys and cable producers do not?

Industry is both a consumer of, and a supplier to, high-tech industries. To reap the benefits of heavy R & D investments, a sustainable level of activities must be developed. This involves not just designing products but also designing processes which provide the most 'manufacturable' design. It requires product and process design capabilities which are close to each other – both organisationally and geographically. Too often, an innovation's benefits are lost because the designer has no control over manufacturing competencies which could help construct a defendable competitive position.

Manufacturing is often the part of the production chain where the greatest share of value is added. It therefore offers the greatest number of possibilities for protecting this value added from competitors. As a result, high-tech companies tend to gravitate towards state of the art producers in any given industry. Chip design and production is stronger in Japan than anywhere else in the world because of the wealth of upstream and downstream companies with which chip producers can associate. Japan has a virtual monopoly on the machinery for chip production, and this is, to a large extent, the consequence of the fact that it supplies some of the world's finest chip customers, both in consumer electronics and industrial applications.

WHAT GENERAL MANAGEMENT NEEDS TO KNOW

Manufacturing matters because it remains an important component of economic activity, because its impact can be felt far beyond the traditional limits of manufacturing industries, and because it is a nurturing ground for new high-tech industries. So general managers should not completely delegate the management of the manufacturing function to a few specialists. Without getting involved in daily operations, any general manager should have enough understanding of the challenges facing manufacturing to contribute to shaping future manufacturing strategies and policies. General managers should also understand the role manufacturing can play in the growth of a company. Hayes & Wheelwright[2] have proposed a simple model characterising the attitude companies have towards manufacturing.

Four approaches to manufacturing

Internally neutral
Some companies would simply rather do without it. If they could pick products off trees and sell them, they would prefer it. But very few products grow on trees and even those that do require a lot of processing before they reach consumers. These companies see themselves condemned to producing, and will develop an attitude

---

[2] Hayes R. H. & Wheelwright S. G., 1984, *Restoring our Competitive Edge*, John Wiley & Sons, New York.

towards manufacturing which is *internally neutral*. They will try to reduce the negative impact that manufacturing has on the business. They will invest in workforce management to avoid strikes. They will manage suppliers to eliminate those that deliver too late, in the wrong quantities, or of the wrong quality. They will manage and maintain plants to avoid supply break downs.

Their basic attitude is negative: 'how do we avoid problems?' In many cases one will see that this type of company will subcontract a good share of production, and will not build up a strong proprietary competence. Amstrad, the British company that designs and sells personal computers and consumer electronics, falls into this category. It subcontracts manufacturing and has virtually no capabilities in the area. It is a risky strategy. It means that competitive advantage resides in design capabilities and control of distribution channels. It is not certain whether Amstrad's strength in these areas is sufficient to allow the company to survive in the long run.

Externally neutral

A second group of companies concluded that their competitors built competitive advantage on manufacturing capabilities. This was true of several European car manufacturers in the second half of the 1980s. Ford, Renault and Volkswagen discovered that Toyota and Honda were making inroads into their markets with better quality products. The growing competitive strength of Japanese car producers was not due to intrinsically superior design, better marketing or more efficient dealer networks – it was the way the car was produced that made the difference.

Awareness of this performance gap made these companies decide to make manufacturing *externally neutral*. The objective was to close the gap by improving performance. But such a strategy is almost doomed to fail. If ambitions are limited to simply closing gaps, risks are high that the gap remains as competitors keep one step ahead. Catching up to better competitors usually leaves companies trailing.

That is exactly what happened to a number of European manufacturers in the 1980s. Only once they overcame the 'follower' attitude did they start improving manufacturing. Current comparisons of European manufacturers' product development and manufacturing processes suggest that they have developed capabilities which stand comparison with their best global competitors. Getting there meant getting rid of a neutral attitude towards manufacturing, and developing a vision of manufacturing as a support function.

Internally supportive

A third group of companies decided that manufacturing should provide a credible support to corporate strategy. Strategy development in these companies is based on functions such as marketing, development or finance. Manufacturing's task is to be *internally supportive*, ensuring processes that fully support strategic company decisions. This may sound obvious. Why would it be otherwise? Perhaps because business strategy imposes many complex demands on manufacturing.

Take the example of companies, such as Benetton or Esprit, producing fashionable ready-to-wear clothes for sophisticated European markets. They launch up to seven collections every year: two for the winter and summer seasons, one for Christmas, and two sports collections. On top of that, these companies must be able to react quickly if the competition launches a new product which catches on with fashion-sensitive consumers. An internally supportive manufacturing function must invest in reducing manufacturing lead times and making the production process flexible. This requires production systems which are efficient with small batch sizes, require low switchover costs, and allow innovations in process design.

It is well known that Benetton copes with the required flexibility and reaction speed by delaying dyeing part of its output until the last step in the production process. That sounds simple, but it requires a great deal of inventiveness to design a process that can dye finished clothes reliably and at high speed.

Process engineers may prefer production without any messy dyeing at the end and with large batch sizes, avoiding having to constantly reset the machine. But the corporate marketing strategy is based on fast reaction, and a company whose manufacturing function is internally supportive must create and develop capabilities that allow the company to react in less then eight days in case the competition comes out with an unexpectedly exciting colour pattern.

Externally supportive

A fourth group of companies goes one step further and turns manufacturing into a key element of business strategy. This does not mean manufacturing drives strategy. But the business strategy fully uses manufacturing's core competencies in creating sustainable competitive advantage. This group of companies is called *externally supportive*.

Hewlett Packard has used its strong manufacturing capabilities extensively. They complement the company's design and marketing, allowing HP to remain a successful computer company into the 1990s, a difficult period during which many of their competitors incurred serious losses. Toyota has, to a large extent, built its success on the qualities and efficiency of its development and production processes. Many German machine tool producers survived thanks to their excellent manufacturing processes.

Manufacturing pays off

These four categories carry a strong message for all managers: success depends on shifting the company's attitude towards manufacturing from a neutral to a supportive one. Why? Because it pays off. In a manufacturing database of about 100 companies for which I have been collecting data since 1986, I have been able to distinguish companies which keep manufacturing neutral from companies that make it a supportive function.

Unsurprisingly, the two groups differ markedly in their approach to manufacturing. Some of the differences are to be expected. The 'supportive' group invests more than the 'neutral' group in employees. They give them more interesting jobs and provide a lot of formal and on-the-job training. They invest more in technology. They do not invest more in standalone technology such as robots or isolated, numerically controlled machines. They put relatively more emphasis on integrating technologies, such as communication links and integrated computer databases. They also invest more in advanced manufacturing programmes such as statistical process control, just-in-time delivery systems or modern performance measurement systems.

Their investments seem to pay off. The database is a longitudinal one, and has data for some of these companies over several years. That allows a comparison of one year's action plans with the following year's results. Comparing attitudes towards manufacturing one year with financial performance measures in later years always leads to the same conclusion. Supportive attitudes pay off by leading to comparatively better financial performance.

If manufacturing is essential to creating sustainable competitive positions, general managers need to understand which levers can be used to improve manufacturing. That is what this book is about. It takes the general manager's viewpoint and describes what needs to be done to evaluate and enhance the strategic role of manufacturing. That does not mean it is not appropriate for the senior manufacturing manager. He will already have reflected upon many of the questions and suggestions addressed, but the structure provided may help to better conceptualise the challenges and the action programmes.

NEW DEFINITIONS OF MANUFACTURING

Understanding the new role of manufacturing means seeing the function as more than the simple transformation of raw materials, components and subassemblies into goods through the use of capital and people. That is too traditional a definition. It has to be looked at as a means of creating customer value in the most productive way possible. But productivity, in this context, also requires a new definition. It is not getting the highest possible output for the lowest input of resources. It is about responding optimally to customer needs through the intelligent deployment of resources.

Responding to the customer's needs requires well balanced portfolios covering cost efficiency, quality, production flexibility and the delivery reliability. The intelligent deployment of resources must recognise that direct labour has, in many manufacturing sites, become a marginal cost factor. Real productivity improvements in resource use are obtained by better usage of capital equipment, more intelligent use of information and better management of materials flow.

This definition of productivity is discussed in detail in Chapter 2. Chapter 3 analyses in more detail the nominator of the productivity relation: the portfolio of outputs in manufacturing. To be responsive to customers we can invest in improved quality, in response speed, in efficient production processes, that allow the lowest prices and the best delivery performance. This is not a neutral choice. It is highly dependent on what the competition is doing.

In the 1980s, the key concept was strategic quality management. Manufacturing's most important task was to provide a high quality product at a reasonably low cost. During this period most European and North American companies were taken by surprise by the performance of Japanese competitors. In the meantime, they seem to have caught up, and quality is losing some of its predominance as a competitive weapon. It has become an absolute minimum requirement.

But that does not mean that everybody is now equal. Some of the leading manufacturers have gone a step further and are creating a new challenge based on the combination of design flexibility and cost efficiency. This is not the only option, and a company cannot escape analysing its future strategic manufacturing agenda. This book provides a mapping tool that can help senior manufacturing managers analyse where they stand vis-a-vis their competitors, and what manufacturing strategy they would like to develop for the future.

In Chapters 4 and 5, two strategic manufacturing missions are developed: strategic quality and cost efficient flexibility. High quality, consistently defect-free production has become the entry point to participating in the competitive game. Companies that want to compete on quality have to go one step further and make the transition from quality assurance to strategic quality management. To understand what strategic quality management entails, these chapters outline a historic overview of the evolution of quality management and introduce a market oriented definition of manufacturing quality. They also briefly discuss what implementing strategic quality management involves.

A second strategic manufacturing mission for the near future is cost efficient flexibility. Flexibility is not a new concept, but the type of flexibility that will soon be demanded differs greatly from the fast reaction and customisation that a small shop could provide. Markets will want fast reaction and a high degree of customisation, but for high volume, low cost consumer products. Manufacturing can play an important role in these developments, but it requires close collaboration with development.

Chapter 5 looks at some of the actions that manufacturing can take, but will mainly focus on the interaction between manufacturing and design. Both quality management and cost efficient flexibility involve factories that live in symbiosis with their partners in integrated networks. Two types of networks will be discussed.

Chapter 6 describes the local network of the factory with its customers, suppliers, local community, product and process engineering and employees. The chapter's essential message is that a factory is part of a larger chain that creates solutions for customers, rather than hardware. That requires removing many existing barriers between the factory and its partners, and implies a more sophisticated network management.

Network management is also the specific topic of Chapter 7, but focuses on the international plant networks. Factories do not operate in isolation, but work in close collaboration with factories around the world. This chapter introduces a helpful concept for designing and managing such networks.

Knowing what to do is great. Implementing it is better. Two aspects of implementation are studied in Chapter 8. Why do some companies have successful manufacturing improvement programmes which have a lasting impact, while others seem to be effective initially, but lose their effect over time? This book suggests that creating lasting improvements requires a particular sequence of improvement programmes.

In Chapter 9, some predictions are made about what tomorrow's manufacturing organisation may look like. What to do in manufacturing is probably relatively easy to determine. The future stars of manufacturing management are those that will be able to implement fastest. In order to speed up implementation, strong direction will be combined with high degrees of freedom and entrepreneurship.

Chapter 10 dwells on the consequences of a strategic view of manufacturing and new manufacturing organisations will have on performance measurement. Well adapted performance measurement systems must measure dynamic rather than static performance, and value creating activities rather than costs. Performance measurement systems must not be seen as a control, but as a tool to enhance the learning and the change in the organisation.

Five or ten years ago, the idea that manufacturing could play an important role in defining and implementing strategy was new. The rediscovery of manufacturing's competitive value was the subject of several articles and books written during the first half of the 1980s. Today, we need to go further. We need to explain how a competitive role is defined and how it can be implemented.

Manufacturing has become too important to be left to manufacturing specialists. The challenge posed by manufacturing strategy goes beyond optimising manufacturing action plans. Responding to the challenge requires a customer oriented view of the transformation process. It will succeed only if the manufacturing function is well integrated with the rest of the company's activities. Stimulating that integration requires general management input. The next chapters aim to assist general managers in formulating the right questions to establish a position of leadership in manufacturing.

SUMMARY

Manufacturing matters because:
- it is an important component of economic activities
- its impact goes beyond the traditionally defined bounds of manufacturing
- it is a nurturing ground for high-tech innovation

General managers should be aware of manufacturing challenges.

A model by Hayes & Wheelwright describes four approaches to manufacturing:
- internally neutral
- externally neutral
- internally supportive
- externally supportive.

This model is important because it demonstrates that manufacturing can pay off when properly managed.

New definitions of manufacturing

The book proposes a new look at manufacturing based on new definitions of what is involved and what is produced.

2 A NEW DEFINITION OF PRODUCTIVITY

Manufacturing's new role is to create a sustainable competitive position. The question, of course, is how? A look at the traditional role of manufacturing best illustrates what needs to be changed and why. It is not only that manufacturing management needs to adapt to a changing environment. The definitions upon which the discipline was built need to be redefined and greater consideration given to the strategic goal of the firm as a whole. Clearly establishing priorities and accurately measuring their implications are the first step to managing manufacturing in the future.

WHAT IS MANUFACTURING MANAGEMENT?

The key to manufacturing management is productivity. Manufacturing is one step in a company's goal of creating customer value – the same value designed by the development function and marketed by the marketing function. Manufacturing transforms raw materials, components and services into a finished product. Manufacturing management works at optimising this transformation process or, in other words, at improving productivity.

Traditional definitions of productivity

Productivity has traditionally been defined as the relationship between input and output in the transformation process. Manufacturing management was devoted to increasing the output for a given input, decreasing the input for a given output, or a combination of the two. But the concepts of input and output were too abstract to be easily applied, so they were quickly translated into something more tangible.

Output was translated into tons of steel, hectolitres of beer, or hundreds of cars produced. Input became units of resources typically used in manufacturing, usually divided into four main categories:

1. *Direct labour:* the number of hours of labour directly allocated to the transformation process.
2. *Capital equipment:* the investment in plant, machinery, or information systems.
3. *Materials:* the raw materials, components, and sub-assemblies which go into the process.
4. *Systems:* the systems which make the manufacturing process function.

The last category, which is somewhat broad, included maintenance, process engineering, manufacturing personnel management, supervison and control systems, as well as other indirect labour activities needed to keep the manufacturing process running smoothly.

This definition is widely used today. This chapter, however, will argue that it is out of date. International organisations such as the

$$\text{Productivity} = \frac{\text{output}}{\text{input}}$$

$$= \frac{\text{volume}}{\text{resources}}$$

$$= \frac{\text{volume}}{(\text{direct labour} + \text{capital equipment} + \text{materials} + \text{systems})}$$

Figure 2.1. Definition of productivity

OECD base their evaluations of productivity on these measurements. Some evaluations are based on even more narrow definitions, limited, for example, to the amount of direct labour. This book aims to demonstrate that this definition is no longer sufficient for managing manufacturing. But readers should remember that many international comparisons are still based on the old definition.

Adapting definitions

For modern manufacturing management, limiting output to volume is no longer viable. It is no longer enough to produce thousands of tons of steel or hectolitres of beer. Today, customers also demand that it be produced at a given level of quality, within an established time frame and delivered to a specified location. The safest, most fuel-efficient airline, with the best meals-to-movie in-flight service, the friendliest stewardesses, the most comfortable waiting lounge and the lowest price quickly becomes valueless when the plane leaves two hours late and makes you miss the crucial management meeting.

The input side has also changed dramatically. The four categories of resources are still valid, but their relative importance has shifted. Industrial engineering textbooks used to assume (some still do) that improving productivity meant reducing the amount of direct labour in the transformation process. So productivity improvement programmes were aimed at replacing direct labour with capital equipment and systems, hoping that the overall value of resources used would decrease.

Generations of engineers were indoctrinated with the first commandment of industrial engineering: 'Thou shalt replace people with machines'. And it worked. Direct labour has been almost entirely squeezed out of the production process. By 1990, direct labour costs was down to 15 per cent of the manufacturing total (Table 2.1).

In many industries, and particularly in assembly processes, direct labour costs as a proportion of total production costs have been reduced to single digits. In personal computer assembly,

	Europe	*United States*	*Japan*
Materials cost	55.3%	53.4%	59.5%
Energy	4.8	4.8	4.0
Direct labour	16.6	13.2	16.3
Capital equipment and overheads	23.4	28.5	20.5

Source: Miller *et al* (1992)

Table 2.1 Manufacturing resource costs as a percentage of total manufacturing cost (1991)

direct labour only represents one or two per cent of total costs. Even in more traditionally labour-intensive processes like clothes manufacturing, direct labour amounts to only six or seven per cent. But definitions of productivity have not yet recognised this dramatic evolution.

Modern manufacturing clearly merits an updated definition of productivity.

A NEW LOOK AT PRODUCTIVITY

A more relevant definition of productivity should encourage manufacturing management to shift its focus from machines to a much more important variable: the customer. Since the goal of the transformation process is to create customer value, this parameter needs to be recognised in definitions of productivity. These definitions also need to reflect other developments such as the shift in the relative weight of different types of resources and the appearance of new kinds of resources.

All this yields the following definition of output: *products and/or services which satisfy customers*. Input will describe *intelligently deployed resources*.

Products include services

This definition clearly situates senior manufacturing managers' challenges. Every word is significant. *Products and/or services* is a

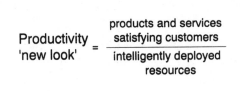

Figure 2.2 *Productivity new look*

formal recognition that products alone are no longer enough, that they are simply part of a larger package which increasingly includes services.

Nobody sells just products anymore. Evidence of the new trend is mushrooming. Computer companies sell solutions, which Digital Equipment calls 'the integrated enterprise'. Volvo no longer sells anything as banal as cars, it sells 'safe transportation at predictable prices'. This explains the company's recent purchase of a large insurance company, allowing it to offer integrated packages to its customers. It includes the car, but also covers services – from financial conditions and after-sales service to warranties and maintenance contracts.

Similarly, customers do not buy just medicine – that is only the visible tip of a very complex iceberg. They buy the guarantee of safety implied by highly sophisticated production systems. The system ensures that a company can instantaneously trace every element of a contaminated pill all the way back through the whole production process to the suppliers. Manufacturing cannot design processes in isolation to the services that come with the product. This example demonstrates that for the tracing service to be provided, the manufacturing function has to integrate information systems at every stage of the production process.

Selling vs. satisfying

The proposed definition of productivity emphasises the fact that a product has to *satisfy* customers. That means more than simply *selling.* Selling something – once – is relatively easy, a good salesman can sell almost anything. The challenge lies in selling so that customers return, and recommend your products to others. This is where manufacturing must focus its attention.

A product should be counted as contributing to productivity only once it has satisfied a customer. Too often, we measure productivity at the factory gate. As soon as a product leaves the factory, manufacturing considers it output. Productivity which measures boxes out the door motivates people to produce more and more boxes. But it may be encouraging the production of boxes nobody wants.

A major American computer company had trouble getting its products (a combination of hardware and software) to its customers on time. One of their key productivity measurements, late deliveries, was constantly sending out warning signals. A concerted logistics management effort soon solved a number of bottlenecks in delivery channels. Although some deliveries still were not on time, the average number of late deliveries fell below target. Many orders even began arriving early.

Measured at the factory door, a significant improvement had been achieved. The only problem was that, for the customer, an early delivery was just as annoying as a late one. The number of orders delivered early or late had increased, without ever being on time. In terms of customer satisfaction, performance had actually deteriorated.

Until we measure output (and through it, productivity) from the customer's perspective, we are not counting realistically.

Customer satisfaction in manufacturing terms

Manufacturing has traditionally used the concept of *missions* to describe its contribution to customer value. Matching mission with strategy is manufacturing management's most significant task. The importance of these missions lies in defining which of the many possible manufacturing targets has priority. What is chosen reflects a company's corporate strategy. Manufacturing can pursue different missions, usually reflecting what customers value most:

- quality
- reliable delivery
- cost efficiency
- customisation
- volume flexibility

BMW, Mercedes or Lexus choose to satisfy customers by offering a high *quality* product. In other cases, such as just-in-time production processes, where the customer's logistics chain is the determining factor, *reliable delivery* will be privileged. Some products, such as petrol, are bought simply on the basis of price, so the manufacturer's key task is to increase *cost efficiency*. Other companies base their strategies on offering a tremendous amount of customisation while others, such as some seasonal industries, are forced by the nature of their business to ensure a degree of *volume flexibility*.

In the automobile industry, customisation is the key priority. A customer's first decision is usually which model to buy. But once that choice is made, the product is customised with a wide range of options. When the rejuvenated Audi 80 was introduced in the autumn of 1991, the company offered 14 base models with different engines and transmission systems. These 14 models could be equipped with 262 colour and interior design combinations. Adding in other options, from central locking and electrically-controlled windows to safety features such as airbags and ABS, there are more than 5.9 trillion different combinations – it must be almost impossible to find two identical Audi 80s on the road.

Customisation is becoming an increasingly generalised phenomenon and a growing number of companies are making it their prime manufacturing mission. Extraordinary variety is now available for everything from hi-fi equipment to mountain bikes. A production facility able to cope with this amount of complexity in assembling customised consumer goods requires a very particular design.

Draught beer producers, on the other hand, are more interested in *volume flexibility*. People drink draught beer when the weather is hot. They drink cocoa when it is cold. This direct relation to temperature, combined with a very short shelf life, means that draught beer has to be produced when it will be consumed. It is almost impossible to create buffer stocks. So the key priority of breweries specialising in draught beer is the ability to increase or decrease output very quickly.

Manufacturers would ideally like to offer cheap, dependable, quality products with lots of customisation and volume flexibility. But realistically, it is not possible – yet – to be best at everything. The technology does not allow it. Some missions impose qualifying levels. A minimum level of quality or flexibility and a maximum level of cost is mandatory, simply to stay competitive. This implies that the missions – and the environment in which they are selected – are fully understood by the manufacturing function.

Manufacturers' objectives in Europe today

The European Manufacturing Futures Survey, conducted over the past nine years at INSEAD and covering the top firms in Europe, illustrates the missions and priorities of European manufacturers today and in the short term.[1]

Table 2.2 shows, in order of importance, what the average European manufacturer considers a priority. The list is more detailed than the five missions described above because it uses more detailed definitions of missions. For example, quality is broken down into three separate concepts:

- defect rate reduction (internal measurement)
- product reliability increase (external market goal)
- high performance product production.

In 1990, these three quality concepts, as well as reliable delivery, were judged to be the top four priorities. Discussions with executives led to the conclusion that the average European manufacturer, in pursuing these goals, is making total quality management, in all its facets, the main manufacturing mission for the 1990s.

---

[1] De Meyer, A. and Ferdows K., 1991, 'Removing the Barriers in Manufacturing', *European Management Journal*, Vol. 9, no. 1, pp. 22–29

Ranking of Competitive Priorities (1990)	Ranking of Competitive Priorities (1992)
1. Offer consistently low defect rates	Offer consistently low defect rates
2. Make dependable delivery promises	Provide reliable/durable products
3. Provide reliable/durable products	Make dependable delivery promises
4. Offer high-performance products or amenities	Profit in price competitive markets
5. Offer fast deliveries	Offer fast deliveries
6. Customise products and services to customer needs	Introduce new products quickly
7. Profit in price competitive markets	Offer high performance products or amenities
8. Introduce new products quickly	Customise products and services to customer needs
9. Provide effective after-sales services	Provide effective product support
10. Offer a broad product line	Provide effective after-sales services
11. Make rapid volume changes	Offer a broad product line
12. Make rapid product mix changes	Make rapid product mix changes
13. Make product easily available	Make rapid design changes
14. Make rapid design changes	Make rapid volume changes
15.	Offer broad distribution

Source: European Manufacturing Futures Survey 1990 and 1992.

Table 2.2 Evolution of competitive priorities in Europe (first is most important)

Speedy delivery ranks immediately next on the list. Competing on price, which implies cost efficiency, was situated in the middle of the ranking. Priorities related to customisation and volume flexibility were ranked near the bottom.

It would seem that the average European manufacturer is content to simply qualify on price, cost and flexibility but aims to compete on total quality. But this may be a little too sweeping a statement. Individual companies pursue very different strategies, and even average companies in homogeneous industries display differences. Companies in electronic product assembly and instruments stress the importance of the rapid introduction of new designs (customisation). Producers of non-durable consumer goods, such as food or toiletries, attach more importance to price competition (cost efficiency).

By comparing this with the 1992 results, the evolution of manufacturing missions in Europe can be measured (See Table 2.2, second column).

Quality remains a top priority for European manufacturers. But compared to 1990, some interesting evolutions can be seen among the top five priorities cited. European manufacturers seem to have become more aware of the necessity of competing on price and delivering quickly and reliably. The introduction of new products is high on the list, placing sixth in 1990, just behind quality, delivery and price. But the ability to rapidly change product design barely appears. Last on the 1990 list, it becomes thirteenth on the 1992 list. European manufacturers see it as a necessity to introduce more and faster new products, but they do not like changing current products too often. This suggests a dislike of product development policies involving small, continuous product improvements (and all the engineering change orders this entails), but a simultaneous recognition that significant changes in products will be introduced ever more rapidly.

The point of this comparison is not to focus on the changes that occur, but rather to highlight that portfolios of competitive priorities do change gradually over time.

The role of general management

Manufacturing missions are a function of business strategy, and as such should be established by general management. Companies must choose which mission, or combination of missions, best defines the parameters on which they wish to compete. This goes well beyond the bounds of the manufacturing function – it has long-term consequences. Whatever the manufacturing mission selected, it will have a direct impact on a company's future flexibility and strategic choice.

Manufacturing is like an oil tanker. Once you have determined its mission, it is not an easy thing to change. Because of the high asset intensity and the number of people it involves, it takes time to change direction. Companies should be careful not to find themselves with a manufacturing function which puts unexpected constraints on corporate strategy.

If an automobile company's strategy is to sell simple cars cheaply and make money on options, it needs an assembly operation that can cope with billions of different combinations. It does not want an extremely efficient assembly operation that does not have the flexibility to manage the sophisticated logistics required to quickly deliver a highly customised car.

Manufacturing's high asset intensity should not, however, become an excuse for immobility. Over the years, manufacturing missions need to be changed and adapted to the competitive environment. Companies have recently been reorienting missions emphasising cost efficiency towards priorities focusing on product quality or customisation. So even oil tankers can change direction. Manufacturing missions are a dynamic, not a static, concept. But their evolution needs to be carefully prepared and directed.

Shifting direction requires more than careful definition and supervision. It demands broad-based support within the company. It takes a long time to implement a change of mission. An example is the time it took large companies to implement and benefit from quality programmes in the 1980s.

Corning Glass, a speciality glass producer invested heavily in quality programmes as early as 1982. The whole company was highly motivated. The top manager expressed his strong support of the programme on a video shown throughout the company. Every directors' meeting had quality management as the first item on its agenda. While the company quickly achieved some minor improvements, it took almost five years to succeed in adapting the company to new priorities. It required a profound change in company culture – including its manufacturing mission – from one which stressed efficiency and technological prowess to one which focused on quality and customer value.

Missions should be chosen carefully and changed strategically.

THE RELATIVE VALUE OF RESOURCES

The shifting relative weight of the four categories of input (direct labour, capital equipment, materials and systems) requires changes in productivity improvement programmes.

The growing importance of capital investments

Generations of manufacturing managers were taught that productivity improvement meant direct labour productivity improvement. The result is that today, the fat in the manufacturing function usually lies elsewhere. Productivity improvement efforts are now concentrating on fighting waste in the use of capital equipment and materials.

Belgium has one of the lowest levels of hours worked, per week and per employee, in the world. Yet it is one of the most productive economies, with a high capital equipment utilisation rate. This is largely due to the flexibility of the direct labour force. It suggests that higher productivity comes more from using an expensive labour force intelligently than it does from squeezing an additional Franc out of its cost. Which is how Belgian industry is able to reduce the cost of its capital investments.

This phenomenon does not only exist at a macroeconomic level. Small companies are often best at obtaining flexibility from their workforces, allowing them to keep expensive machines working constantly. Salmson, a 700-employee French producer of pumps and water circulators, introduced a system of adaptable working weeks. For the most part, working weeks vary from 33 to 43 hours, depending on demand. So rather than having a fixed working week, with employees occasionally not having anything to do and at other times needing the assistance of temporary help, flexibility was established within the company's own workforce. Some people work in two six-hour shifts, others in three six-hour shifts, still others work in four or five shift systems. The result is that equipment is fully utilised, turning 155 hours per week. The rest is not down time, it is used for maintenance.

What is true for equipment is also true for materials. In many assembly operations, materials and components represent over 80 per cent of costs. Reducing waste by improving quality and statistical process control can have a significant impact on assembly productivity. The CEOs of 230 top European companies surveyed by McKinsey and Co. in 1988 believed that their companies' gross margins could increase by an average of 17 per cent and variable costs could decrease by 35 per cent if 'Total Quality Management' practices were actually employed.

A new resource: information

No one will deny that information has always played an important part in managing production. Market information has always helped determine production capacity and master schedules. Process technology data has long contributed to improving the production process. But now there is a fundamental shift because information is emerging as a separate production resource.

To react quickly to changing market conditions and to respond better to customer requests, manufacturing has brought information to the factory floor. In a just-in-time world, filters between customers and producers are no longer tenable. Sales teams, market forecasters, market planners and production schedulers fulfil important functions but they can also distort communication between users and producers. This fundamental relationship must be carefully protected from possible distortions by other contributors.

Information has also been integrated directly into the production process itself. Data on technology, markets, suppliers and the environment contribute to competitive policy decisions. Information has become more than a production support, it has become a resource in its own right. Cut the information supply and many factories shudder to a directionless halt.

Fashion producers or supply networks like Marks & Spencer's know that any interruption in information means trouble for production. This sector used to deal with two fashion collections a year, but they now manage at least seven. Summer and Winter have evolved into four seasons plus a Christmas collection and two sports collections, one for sun and one for snow. So companies like Marks & Spencer's only have about 35 days to evaluate, design, produce and market each collection. That means that if they are one day late in reacting to the latest fashion trend, they quickly lose their competitive edge. Timeliness in this industry is all. And it all depends on regular and up-to-the-minute information flows.

Information used to be considered a free resource. Because there was no cost attached, it seemed to be something that flowed around quite naturally. As information becomes a production resource, however, it has to be treated differently. Like any other resource, like people who are selected, trained and promoted, information will have to managed. Many questions will require precise and tested answers:

- how is information required by production selected and accessed and how often?
- how is it stored?
- how is it improved?
- how do companies learn from existing information?
- how can databases be built describing processes, market responses, supplier networks and other essential competitive knowledge?

Manufacturing resources no longer just mean labour. Every input needs to be evaluated and included in the process and in its management.

Suppliers as corporate resource

Suppliers also affect our changing view of resources. In the past, productivity definitions only took into account resources owned and controlled by a company. Companies evaluated the productivity of their own direct labour, capital equipment or materials utilisation. But this hardly optimised the process.

Factories do not operate in a vacuum. They are integrated into a value chain which creates value for the end user. To produce that value in the most effective way, companies not only have to improve the productivity of their own plants but will have to contribute to improving the productivity of the whole chain. That means developing partnerships with suppliers and distributors. Investments in process technology and improvements in materials utilisation should be carried out in conjunction with these partners.

Producing a book, for example, represents 15 per cent in production costs, 35 per cent for the editor and author's copyright and 50 per cent for distribution. Production costs cover paper and supplies (50 per cent), binding (26 per cent) and printing (19 per cent). Trying to increase productivity by focusing on the three per cent represented by the printing would not make much sense. Productivity gains can only be made if the whole chain, including the author, the editor, the printer and the paper supplier cooperate to give the final customer better value.

MEASURING PRODUCTIVITY

Changes in the definition of productivity require changes in the way it is measured. The systems used to monitor productivity have to match all the other variables described above: the manufacturing mission, the type of resources used, and their relative weights.

This is easier than commonly thought. Each mission has a dedicated performance measure. The ones for quality or cost efficiency are well known. Reliable delivery can be measured by tracking on-time delivery, death on arrival (when the ON button has no impact), number of rush orders, etc. Flexibility can be approximated as the length of set-up times, number of product variations, start-up speed, ability to cope with engineering change orders, etc. The problem is not only defining appropriate measures, but integrating them into existing accounting and control systems.

The 'New Look' productivity definition requires three changes in control systems:

- the ability to define and integrate effectiveness measures which correspond to the manufacturing mission

- resource allocation mechanisms that cope with the changing relative importance of different production resources
- ratios that measure change, rather than fixed targets.

The first two requirements can be partially solved with modern control systems based on activity-based costing, discussed in Chapter 10.

The third requirement remains a challenge. Analog Devices offer an example. Figure 2.3 shows the on-time delivery performance of nine production facilities. Comparing them relative to a specific target, factory D seems to be the best performer. It achieves the target and reduces the variability surrounding it. Taking dynamic factors into account, however, it is factory C which performs best. It is the quickest in reducing the number of late deliveries by 50 per cent.

If factories have to live up to their new productivity task, this dynamic view of performance is key.

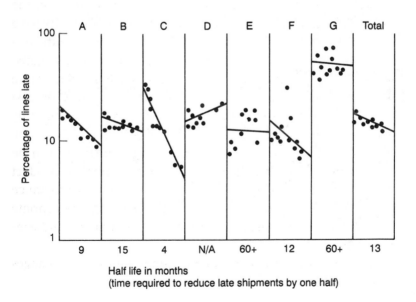

Figure 2.3 Analog devices on-time customer service performance monthly data (August 1987–July 1988)

SUMMARY

A new look at productivity
Today's market conditions impose greater customer focus, leading to new definitions:
- Output = products and services which satisfy clients
- Input = intelligently deployed resources
- Products = products + services

Productivity should not be measured in function of internal criteria but based on customer satisfaction.

Manufacturing missions
Missions focus manufacturing's priorities to support corporate strategies (e.g.quality, reliable delivery, price, customisation, volume flexibility). They need to be selected carefully because they are slow to change.

The relative value of resources
The relative weight of manufacturing resources is shifting, pushing productivity programmes to adapt. Define the relative weight of your company's manufacturing resources.

Measuring productivity
The 'new look' definition of productivity implies three changes in measurement systems:
- defining and integrating measures which correspond to the manufacturing mission
- setting up allocation processes which recognise the relative importance of production resources
- establishing ratios to measure change rather than aiming for fixed targets.

3 PUTTING MISSION IN MOTION

No magic formulae exist for determining manufacturing missions, nor are there standard approaches for particular industries. Missions involve more than the manufacturing function because their direction depends on corporate strategy – and management. There are, however, lessons to be learned from what others have done to structure and manage the evolution of missions.

EVOLVING PRIORITIES

The link between strategy and mission

The concept of manufacturing strategy, with its implied choice of manufacturing missions, is more than 25 years old. Defining manufacturing strategies requires finding a relation between corporate strategy and the design of a manufacturing system. This involves two types of choices: those concerning organisation and those related to infrastructure. Organisational considerations include elements such as factory location, production capacity, process technologies, and degrees of vertical integration. Infrastructure decisions involve quality management systems, human resource management in the plant, organisation of the manufacturing function, control systems, flow of goods and information, and the way new products are introduced into manufacturing.

Ensuring that decisions on these issues fit into the context of a company's corporate strategy is not always straightforward. It requires what might be called a 'transformer': the key principles of corporate strategy have to be transformed into ideas and guidelines that manufacturing people understand. Wickham Skinner's seminal work showed that this 'transformation' lies in the choice of manufacturing missions.

Defining manufacturing strategies consists of choosing a portfolio of missions (both order-winning and qualifying) which best fits corporate goals. Once the portfolio is determined, choices about structure and infrastructure in manufacturing become obvious. If the company had a cost leadership strategy, it is clear that the order-winning manufacturing mission be cost efficiency. That choice translates into a factory location in a low-cost labour area, a highly standardised production process, big production volumes yielding economies of scale, and a high degree of control – if not ownership – of suppliers. It also implies limited product introductions, very tight cost control systems, etc.

In the 1960s and 1970s, companies tended to choose only one order winning mission, and would be satisfied with a qualifying level for the other missions. But over the last 25 years, companies have defined increasingly wider and more strategic missions for their manufacturing functions.

Cost efficiency first

During the 1970s, most companies' manufacturing missions stuck to a limited number of generic manufacturing strategies. The most common was low cost production. Given the definition of productivity at the time, manufacturing companies naturally made cutting production costs their top priority. It was not that companies were not committed to quality or technological leadership. But they invested in them only once they had achieved results from cost reduction efforts. Commitment to quality certainly existed at General Motors, Ford and Volkswagen. But it intervened only once costs had been calculated.

An alternative approach was to choose market niches where price was largely irrelevant. Producers of exclusive cars such as Mercedes-Benz or Rolls-Royce were highly committed to quality, but they expected their customers to be highly insensitive to price.

Combining missions

The big shock came in the late 1970s, when a few (mainly Japanese) companies revealed that high quality and low cost were not necessarily mutually exclusive. They convincingly demonstrated that total quality was in fact the foundation of cost efficiency. A growing number of companies quickly became committed to continuous improvements in product design and a better understanding of the overall process. This led to reductions in materials waste, quality inspection, control procedures, warranty claims, after-sales service and repair costs, and contributed to reducing total product cost. In the process, manufacturers discovered that they were not limited to pursuing a single mission – they could combine two of them.

It has taken American companies a long time – and European companies even longer – to understand and assimilate the effects of quality and its consequences on cost reduction. During the 1980s, the attitudes of European companies underwent a significant evolution. From an attitude of 'our quality is the best and customers are willing to pay for it', they began to think that 'we don't really need to change our approach but let's adopt some of these interesting quality tools and techniques'. Now, they have finally realised that 'if we don't completely change our thinking, we won't survive'.

This is a positive evolution, although it may not have come about fast enough. Paradoxically, European companies may have been slower than their North American counterparts in reacting to the quality challenge precisely because of their traditional commitment to high performance products and market quality.

Meanwhile . . . in Japan

Catching up with the quality levels of global competitors is like running after a moving target. While European companies were discovering total quality management, their counterparts in Asia, and to some extent in the United States, were trying a new combination: cost efficiency and customisation. The sum of the two was the ability to quickly introduce consecutive generations of new products without incurring high introductory or start-up costs. It also implied production processes allowing overhead and design investments to be depreciated over smaller volumes.

The European and North American car industries insist that, for any basic model, they need to sell 2,000,000 cars to recuperate their investments. Large volume Japanese car producers need only 500,000 cars. This enables them to change models more often, which in turn develops their capacity to respond quickly to changing market requirements.

Should everyone then aim for this particular combination of cost efficiency and customisation? Definitely not. For particular companies, in particular industries, it may be necessary, but simple imitation should be approached cautiously. Introducing manufacturing strategies developed several years ago in Japan cannot be a winning strategy. New strategies are already knocking at the factory door.

The latest trends

These new strategies can be summarised as *globalising production networks* and *creating customer value*. For Japan, both represent fundamental departures from past policies. The traditional Japanese production network was like a star: a strong centre extended its rays into large, foreign markets. At the end of each ray were sales offices, or limited production facilities responsible for final assembly of completely knocked-down products, local market adjustments, and testing.

Japanese companies have now started setting up foreign plants which do more than simply the final assembly and testing, typical of the 'screwdriver' plants built in the 1970s and 1980s. Today, one finds Japanese factories in Europe and the US creating significant value. Some even carry out product development. Managing these new networks, where each node has an equivalent weight in the amount of value created, poses a whole new set of internationalisation challenges which are covered in Chapter 7.

The 'creating customer value' movement is also a change. Up

until recently, Japanese companies based their approach on the production of standardised mass-produced products which met the average customer's requirements. New, alternative strategies integrating total quality, cost efficiency and customisation are now being developed.

This combination of three different missions is totally unknown to production managers. Production planning systems, control systems or process technologies needed to react quickly to changing customer demands with a high quality; low cost product are simply not yet available from traditional equipment vendors.

CHOOSING MISSIONS – AMERICAN, EUROPEAN AND JAPANESE APPROACHES

Understanding the competition is essential in preparing effective business strategies. The same is true for establishing competitive manufacturing missions. It requires establishing a benchmarking system which monitors what the competition is doing or preparing.

The Global Manufacturing Futures Project, published by J. G. Miller et al.[1] yields data on what other manufacturing companies are doing. Tables 3.1a and 3.1b present some of the key results.

The first table shows how the average European, North American or Japanese company ranks its manufacturing missions, or competitive manufacturing priorities. Asked what their organisation wanted to emphasise as competitive priorities for their manufacturing units over the next five years, senior manufacturing managers revealed their companies' short and medium-term preferences.

The previous chapter analysed some of the European data. In 1990, the average European manufacturer emphasised total quality first, issues related to cost efficiency second, and flexibility last. The most striking result observed in this table is that there are actually many similarities across the three regions. In Japan and

---

[1] see Miller, J.G., De Meyer, A. and Nakane, J., 1992, 'Global Benchmarking in Manufacturing', *Business One Irwin*, Homewood, Illinois.

	Europe	Japan	North America
1.	Offer consistently low defect rates	Provide reliable/durable products	Offer consistently low defect rates
2.	Make dependable delivery promises	Make dependable delivery promises	Make dependable delivery promises
3.	Provide reliable/durable products	Make rapid design changes	Provide reliable/durable products
4.	Offer high-performance products or amenities	Offer consistently low defect rates	Offer high-performance products and amenities
5.	Offer fast deliveries	Customise products and services to customer needs	Profit in price competitive markets
6.	Customise products and services to customer needs	Offer fast deliveries	Offer fast deliveries
7.	Profit in price competitive markets	Profit in price competitive markets	Provide effective product support
8.	Provide effective product support	Offer high-performance products or amenities	Offer a broad distribution
9.	Introduce new products quickly	Provide effective after-sales services	Introduce new products quickly
10.	Provide effective after-sales services	Make rapid volume changes	Customise products and services to customer needs
11.	Offer a broad product line	Provide effective product support	Provide effective after-sales services
12.	Make rapid volume changes	Offer a broad product line	Make rapid product mix changes
13.	Make rapid mix changes	Offer a broad distribution	Offer a broad product line
14.	Offer a broad distribution	Make rapid product mix changes	Make rapid design changes

Source: Global Manufacturing Futures Survey

Table 3.1a Competitive priorities for large manufacturers (1990)

Competitive strengths in order of decreasing importance

Europe	Japan	North America
Strengths		
Provide reliable/durable products	Provide reliable/durable products	Provide reliable/durable products
Offer consistently low defect rates	Offer consistently low defect rates	Offer consistently low defect rates
Offer high-performance products or amenities	Make dependable delivery promises	Offer high-performance products or amenities
Provide effective product support	Customise products and services to customer needs	Provide effective after-sales services
Make dependable delivery promises	Make rapid volume changes	Provide effective product support
Weaknesses		
Make rapid volume changes	Offer a broad product line	Make rapid volume changes
Make rapid design changes	Offer high-performance products	Profit in price competitive markets
Profit in price competitive markets	Make rapid design changes	Make rapid design changes
Introduce new products quickly	Profit in price competitive markets	Introduce new products quickly

Source: Global Manufacturing Futures Survey

Table 3.1b Five major strengths and four major weaknesses for large manufacturers (1990)

North America, quality issues also earn top ranking, and most flexibility issues again find themselves at the bottom. It is the differences which, however minor, offer food for thought.

For North American manufacturers, creating and managing a broad distribution network is considered a slightly more important issue than it is by either the Japanese or the Europeans. This can be explained by market conditions in North America, which remains the world's largest homogeneous market, with the greatest degree of free competition. Being able to quickly reach the whole market is more important to a US manufacturer than it is to many European manufacturers who can launch products in small geographic markets or market niches.

In Europe, the top priority is consistently producing a defect-free product. For the average Japanese producer, however, the top 'quality' priority is the reliability of a product in the market. This suggests that the two groups are at different stages of quality management development. The European group, more inward looking, is concentrating on coming to terms with internal action programmes yielding better quality. The Japanese group is focusing outward, more concerned with improving the performance of products in the market.

Another difference is the ranking given to the ability to rapidly change product design. In Europe and North America, it is at the bottom of the list of priorities. In the Japanese list, it ranks third out of 14. This simple term covers a wealth of diverse challenges. It includes coping with engineering change orders, starting up production very quickly, redeploying production processes in subsequent generations of rejuvenated or redesigned products. It supposes an organisation that adapts to constant change and that preserves understanding gained through experience across generations of new products.

Comparative strengths and weaknesses

Intentions are only half the picture. Determining manufacturing missions and the policies that put them into action also implies comparing them with what the competition is doing.

Table 3.1b shows how manufacturers perceive themselves in comparison with their best competitor. The 'best competitor' is not necessarily the largest. Rather, it is the most threatening – the most competent, in manufacturing terms. This is, of course, a highly subjective judgement. The graphs (figures 3.1a and 3.1b) help to interpret data on current strengths and weaknesses compared with future objectives.[2]

Analysing the graph concerning them should make European manufacturers somewhat uneasy. As a group, they plan to emphasise the consistent production of reliable, defect-free, high performance products. They do not consider it crucial to be able to rapidly change product designs. Europeans consider themselves to be very good at the first point, but they are not, in their own estimation, very strong on the second. In other words, they think they are good at what counts for the future. And they believe that

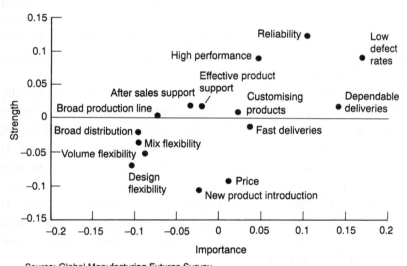

Source: Global Manufacturing Futures Survey

Figure 3.1a Competitive priorities vs. strengths: European futures survey (1990)

[2] The data to produce this graph comes from Miller, J.G. et al (1992). The method of presenting similar data in this way was introduced in J. G. Miller, A. Amano, A. De Meyer, K. Ferdows, J. Nakane, A. Roth, 1989, Closing the Competitive Gaps, in Ferdows K. (Ed), *Managing International Manufacturing*, North Holland, New York.

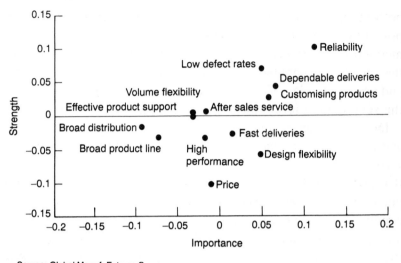

Source: Global Manuf. Futures Survey

Figure 3.1b   Competitive priorities vs. strengths: Japan futures survey (1990)

what they are not good at will be of little significance. Are they lucky? Or complacent?

Overstating the point, one could say that European manufacturers are pleased with themselves. Competitive priorities judged important in the short term happen to be the ones where their strengths are greatest. The priorities where they feel they are not quite up to par, just happen to be those of little importance.

This complacency is perhaps understandable in the context of the survey's timing. The data was gathered during the first semester of 1990. It was a period of Europhoria: Eastern European markets were opening, healthy 1989 profit figures were being published, and the EC's unified market was far enough away not to be worrying.

One would expect that no company would position itself competitively on irrelevant priorities (the items in the top left-hand corner of the graph). A whole series of competitive priorities should appear in the top right-hand quadrant. These are the strengths on which companies will compete, today and in the future. But one would expect at least one or two priorities in the bottom right-hand quadrant. This covers yet-to-be-developed priorities in areas needing improvement which are considered medium-term competitive priorities. It is essential that the priorities on which companies will be competing tomorrow be defined and prepared today. Yet for the average European manufacturer, this set remains sadly empty.

Do other manufacturers define it better? The graph for the average Japanese manufacturer is more complex (see Figure 3.1b). There is less concentration around the diagonal, meaning that perceived strengths and weaknesses are less correlated with perceived importance. And one may wonder about their ability to combine price competition, rapid design changes, high performance product production and rapid delivery. Is this then what is in the making: rapid sequences of efficiently produced, quickly delivered, top-of-the-range products? Perhaps. It is certainly true for some Japanese producers of sophisticated hi-fi equipment or cars. But it is too easy to generalise on the basis of limited input.

PROACTIVE MANUFACTURING MISSIONS

This analysis of empirical data leads to establishing a simple guideline for developing a company's manufacturing missions. It consists of five steps:

1. Determine short and medium-term competitive priorities in manufacturing

Identify strengths the company will need to develop to compete in its industry over the next five years. The list of fifteen items used in the Manufacturing Futures Survey may serve as a point of reference. Alternatives can be used as long as they integrate the five basic categories:

- quality
- reliable deliveries
- cost efficiency

- customisation
- volume flexibility.

The list in itself, of course, is not enough. Relative importance has to be attached to each item so they must be ranked in order of priority. It makes no sense to make trade-offs or to include only those items which allow the company to qualify or win orders. These may be useful in later analyses, but at this stage it is important to get corporate agreement on priorities.

2. Benchmark manufacturing capabilities compared with the best competitor

This requires two difficult tasks: determining the best competitor and establishing comparisons on each competitive priority. Often, surrogates have to be used for information on competitor capabilities because actual data is not always available. Data on real volume flexibility, for example, or actual number of production defects may not be available. But instead, the variation of delivery lead time in function of demand could be measured. Or the number of defects in the market could be a surrogate for internal quality performance.

Just trying to carry out the benchmarking process makes companies more aware of what it is they want to benchmark. It may also contribute to creating intelligence systems to better understand competitors. The result of this step is a ranking of strengths and weaknesses.

3. Map short- and medium-term capabilities with perceived strengths and weaknesses

As in the empirical analysis, this leads to a clearer view of a company's position: wasted efforts (top left corner), current competitive base (top right), future competitive plans (bottom right), and black holes (bottom left) in manufacturing capabilities.

4. Determine where the company needs to move to on the map

Such a map is not static. What movements must be initiated? How does a company move from a position of relative weakness to a position of relative strength? Certainly not by waiting until the needed strength becomes more important and the company's relative weakness more apparent. It requires taking a calculated gamble on what the required priorities will be and by proactively developing the appropriate strengths.

5. Translate into a Portfolio of Manufacturing Missions

The analysis of the map should lead to a definition of current and future order winning and qualifying missions. As suggested earlier in the chapter, one should transform those into action plans for manufacturing.

SUMMARY

Linking corporate strategy and manufacturing missions
- traditionally, missions focused on low cost production
- then the quality movement combined low cost with quality
- today, the new challenge is pursuing multiple missions, such as total quality, cost efficiency and customisation

The latest trends heralding the next step are:
- globalising production networks
- creating customer value.

Competitive comparisons – American, European and Japanese approaches
Manufacturing priorities differ across regions.
- Europe: producing defect-free products.
- Japan: product reliability in the market.
- US: broad distribution networks and time to market.

Pro-active manufacturing missions

Five steps to a manufacturing mission.

(i)   Set short and medium-term priorities.

(ii) Benchmark capabilities compared to best competitor.

(iii) Map short and medium-term capabilities as well as strenghts and weaknesses.

(iv) Determine where company needs to go.

(v)   Translate into a portfolio of missions.

4 QUALITY IS NOT ENOUGH

Customers take good quality products for granted. High quality, defect-free production today is simply the foundation on which competitiveness can be built. Pursuing product quality as a source of competitive advantage was a valid manufacturing strategy in the 1970s or 1980s, but now it can only be a point of departure for more ambitious goals.

This does not mean that quality management can be taken for granted. It should remain an important priority for every senior manager for two reasons. First, quality is an ever-moving target, and reaching a given objective will only ever be a temporary respite. Secondly, because strategic quality management is the basis of all other strategic manufacturing activities. This is why *Business Week* asserts in its special issue on quality management[1] that 'for the 1990s and far beyond, quality must remain the priority for business'.

THE THREE STAGES OF QUALITY MANAGEMENT

Any overview of quality management will describe its evolution in three stages.

1. Quality as corrective action

Quality management began as corrective action. It was seen as avoiding a specific problem: the occurrence of defects in the

---

[1] *Business Week*, December 2, 1991, pp. 17–64.

market. Corrective actions were referred to as quality control, characterised by inspections at checkpoints in the production process or of incoming supplier deliveries. This approach led to little investment being made in process development and much attention being paid to rework. Unacceptable quality performance was addressed by radical restructuring. Quality control was the 'pars pro toto' for quality management, and was often delegated to a staff department. The whole approach was based on an unjustified economic trade-off between costs of quality control and opportunity costs in the market.

Figure 4.1 explains the trade-off in a simplistic two dimensional way. Two different types of cost are involved: quality control costs and quality opportunity costs. These costs are typically plotted according to the number of defects that reached the market.

The more defects allowed in the market, the less had to be spent on quality control actions such as incoming or outgoing inspection or rework. But the more defects in the market, the higher quality opportunity costs rose. These included warranty costs or advertising costs to counter the negative impact of defects on market share.

Industrial engineers optimised the production process by minimising the total cost of quality management. This led to an

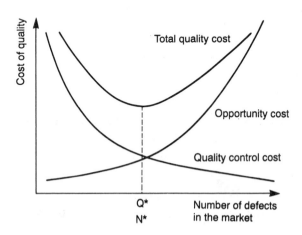

Figure 4.1   Quality trade-off

optimal level of quality (indicated by Q^*). Many people based their approaches or acceptance procedures on this simple trade-off. Many of these must have realised that optimal quality levels implied optimal levels of defects.

This may have made sense if the number of defects was higher than the optimal one (to the right of the optimal quality level Q^*). But what if the company produced less than this optimal number (to the left of Q^*)? Did the number of defects have to increase for the company to be operating optimally? It sounds strange, but allowing for slippage made life very easy for operating managers!

2. Quality as Opportunity

Quality management gradually evolved from trying to correct problems to creating opportunities. The work of quality specialists such as Deming and Juran was extremely influential. Some companies, particularly Japanese ones, discovered that by focusing on process, through Deming's statistical process control or through Juran's total quality management, they could provide high quality products at low cost.

> A 1981 Japanese External Trade Organisation (JETRO) report notes that 'most analyses of productivity growth in the Japanese economy suggest that continued rapid rise in output per man-hour in the manufacturing sector has primarily been a result of such factors as a high rate of capital investment. In recent years, however, increasing attention has been drawn to (modern quality management techniques) as a further factor contributing to . . . not only quality control, but also productivity increase, safety and employee morale'.

The high quality/low cost combination had always seemed impossible. Higher quality in the market had always supposed higher manufacturing costs, going beyond an optimal quality level. So was it a trick, window-dressing, or simply luck? That was a question often asked in the 1970s. What seemed to go against common sense at the time turned out to be simply good process management.

So was the trade-off of Figure 4.1 totally ill-founded? Not really,

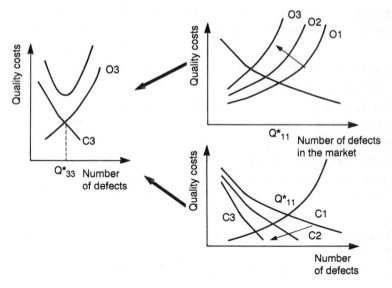

Figure 4.2 Dynamic view of quality management

but it was a static view of the curves. Figure 4.2. explains what happens with a dynamic view of the quality trade-off.

Manufacturers lived under the impression that quality control costs were static, as though it were a law of nature. To reduce the number of defects to under 1 per cent, you needed a given number of quality inspectors. To bring them below 0.1 per cent, you needed more quality inspectors. But they ignored that the quality cost curve itself could be moved – from C_1 to C_2 or even C_3.

It was also soon discovered that the quality opportunity cost curve was not as static as once thought. Under the influence of competitors with higher quality at comparable prices, consumers became more demanding, moving the opportunity cost curve from position O_1 to O_2 or O_3. The result was that the optimal quality level moved drastically to the left, approaching zero.

Why so much emphasis on these simple graphs? Because they suggest the tasks needed to move from the optimal quality level to the left of the graph, a position of lower optimal defect rates. Pushing the quality cost curves down (moving from C_1 to C_3) requires a strong focus on process engineering: controlling and stabilising the process to improve production, quality planning in product and process design, continuous improvement activities, etc.

Increasing the opportunity costs of insufficient quality (moving from O_1 to O_3), reveals very different perceptions of the potential offered by quality in the market. The choice is between imposing a steeper opportunity curve on competitors, or letting the competition create the challenge.

In the 1960s, Europeans had a slightly steeper opportunity curve than the competitors. Catering to customers who valued quality, they could spend more money on control procedures. Graphically, European manufacturers' optimal quality was positioned to the left of most of their competitors. But over time, in industry after industry, overseas competitors have responded by developing expertise in pushing quality cost curves downwards, and for the same price, pushing the Europeans' opportunity cost curves higher and higher.

3. Strategic quality management

Whatever the dynamics of the curves, the optimum quality level never seems to be zero. Is 'zero defects' then just a slogan? Figure 4.3 explores what happens when a magnifying glass is brought to bear on this mythic objective. When markets near zero defects, the curves dramatically change form. The cost curve, rather than being asymptotic with the vertical axis, actually goes down. Getting the variability of the process completely under control, and understanding the process so totally that infallible predictions can be made about output, leads to dramatic reductions in the cost of guaranteeing quality.

Inspection of outgoing products would no longer be needed. Supplier reactions would be such that verification and quality inspection could be forgotten. Slight deviations in machine performance would be detected and adjusted immediately. It is a world where defects and errors completely disappear. If any part of an assembled product differs from specifications, computerised controls automatically adjust the dimensions of the other parts to compensate for the deviation. It is a world where quality is created automatically, almost without effort.

The cost curve is not alone in undergoing a dramatic reversal. The opportunity curve also behaves unexpectedly. It is considered normal that the opportunity curve goes through zero: zero defects should mean zero opportunity costs. But Figure 4.3 suggests that achieving zero defects not only reduces costs, it actually creates benefits. A product with a good quality record in the market creates an image which supports the introduction of subsequent generations. The fact that Sony is one of the most recognised brands around the world is an example of these quality opportunities.

Manufacturing quality contributes to brand recognition, thereby directly affecting marketing. The impact of zero defects goes well beyond manufacturing variables and becomes a truly strategic achievement.

The unexpected behaviour of these two curves changes the optimal level of quality. The economically optimal quality level (Q^*) defined earlier was only a local optimum. A second optimum (Q^{**}) exists at the zero defect level. It is this last optimum level which is the goal of zero defect movements.

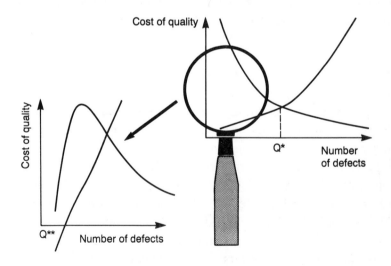

Figure 4.3 Looking through a magnifying glass

The implications

From being an opportunity, quality can be transformed into a strategic weapon that can be wielded in the market place to devastating effect. One moves from a situation where we had a cheaper way of eliminating the defects in the product, to a situation where the 'effortless' management of quality becomes the basis for a situation where we can create and introduce products which are propelled by our quality image, and which if well designed, provide better value for the customer, and consequently 'delight' them.

Shifting quality assurance from opportunity to strategic quality management is more than semantics. With zero defects, quality assurance has attained its goal. In so doing, it loses its value as a manufacturing mission. Quality management becomes an exercise in maintaining and updating existing procedures.

Strategic views of quality will be needed the moment the zero defect level is reached. That is when managers can ask how to use quality capabilities to improve customer value. Once companies repeatedly produce perfect television sets, they can start working on how to introduce rapid sequences of variations and improvements, which will create more value to individual customers. Defining and maintaining that process of matching process capabilities with market demand is the senior manager's challenge.

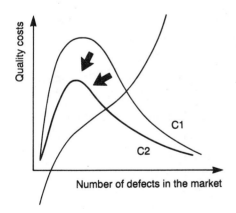

Figure 4.4 Continuing effort in quality management

The second implication is suggested by the remaining hurdle. As suggested in Figure 4.4, continuing efforts in product and process design can push the quality cost curve down from C1 to C2. But the hurdle, or 'quality hill', will remain. If a company wants to move from local optimum Q* to zero defects, they would like to find the shortcut which would save them from having to go over the hill. But so far, that is impossible. There are no short cuts. Companies have to invest in quality management to conquer the peak of the quality hill and discover the valley of zero defects behind it.

Conquering it usually requires significant cultural reforms. Everyone in the organisation must have access to the quality strategy, and understand their role in it. As James Teboul writes in an excellent overview of quality management:[2] '[This cultural reform] is not just to give the normal satisfaction the client is entitled to expect but to build the competitive advantage which will make the difference and delight the customer. Thus the customer is reintegrated into the overall production and delivery process, and the employees become not just responsible to their line managers, but are brought face to face with the authority of the client and the market'.

Making this happen requires a very different organisation, integrating all the value-creating parts of the company, from marketing and production to development.

SQUARING THE CIRCLE – MATCHING CAPABILITIES WITH THE MARKET

Strategic quality management's role is to ensure that manufacturing adapts to changing market requirements. James Teboul has described this as squaring the circle. He depicts market requirements as a circle and the company's offering as a square. The circle is the target, the square the result of the company's design efforts and its ability to manufacture the product accordingly. The square and circle will, of course, never cover exactly the

---

[2] Teboul, J. 1990, *Managing Quality Dynamics*, Prentice Hall, New York.

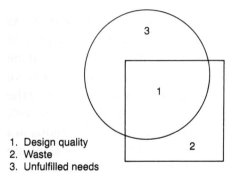

1. Design quality
2. Waste
3. Unfulfilled needs

Figure 4.5 Squaring the circle

same area. It is not even necessary to match needs perfectly, but it is necessary to 'square the circle' at any given moment better than one's competitors.

Defining the circle

Defect-free production means producing a perfect square. Figure 4.6 shows that some defects – in the part of the square which lies outside of the circle – will have no effect on customer satisfaction. They may be a bit of a nuisance, but not enough to influence customer decisions.

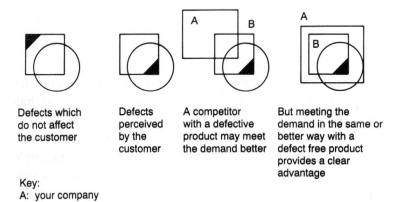

Defects which
do not affect
the customer

Defects
perceived
by the
customer

A competitor
with a defective
product may meet
the demand better

But meeting the
demand in the same or
better way with a
defect free product
provides a clear
advantage

Key:
A: your company
B: the competitor

Figure 4.6 Types of defects

Take a product such as a reclining chair. The reclining mechanism may break down after 15 years, but this is probably not relevant to the customer. The leather upholstering or the foam used to fill the cushions is likely to deteriorate after less than 10 years. There is not much interest in increasing the longevity of the mechanism.

Quality improvement in irrelevant features, or features which far exceed customer requirements does not contribute to better market positioning. Investing in manufacturing capabilities to improve reclining mechanisms may have indirect and important rewards for manufacturing process or culture, but is not essential for meeting customer needs.

On the other hand, customers do not want to find unidentifiable objects in their beer and they may not like scratches on the bottle. Investing in better computerised vision control methods to improve sediment control or analysing the production and distribution system to avoid scratched bottles is moving the square to an area where it starts to overlap with the circle. Kirin, the leading Japanese beer brewer, has refined the quality management of its beer bottles to such an extent that its computerised control systems now find applications in the production of fluid pharmaceuticals.

Managing the square

Getting the square to completely cover the circle may be impossible, inappropriate, or both. It may also be too costly. Total squaring of the circle always leads to four corners hanging outside, symbolising the investment in unnecessary specifications. Strategic quality management aims at improving the square, and optimising the overlap between products and market requirements, rather than realising total coverage of the circle.

What does optimising the overlap imply? Although a company competes with a very well-designed square, Figure 4.6 shows that it may not meet customer requirements as well as a competitor's less attractive square. That would indicate that a product is perfect but nobody wants it, like a fridge in Antarctica.

American automobile producers argue that their cars meet the same quality standards as most Japanese cars. They have, it is true, made vast improvements in their square, but have lost sight of the circle. General Motors invested heavily throughout the 1980s in manufacturing capabilities. It now has path-breaking technology as well as new and improved relationships with suppliers, dealers and employees. In short, it got its manufacturing act together, and even won the 1990 Malcolm Baldridge National Quality Award for its Cadillac division. But at the same time, GM retains five car divisions – Cadillac, Buick, Oldsmobile, Pontiac and Chevrolet – which reflect socio-economic segments of at least 15 years ago. Are they adapted to today's market where people choose a car to reflect lifestyles as well as buying power? The circle has changed.

Circles keep circling round and customer needs will change continuously. Limiting quality management to the square will only make manufacturing squarer and less adapted to customers. Strategic quality management requires creating mechanisms that improve the square while following the movements of the circle.

What does this imply? An investment in improved quality assurance is a good start. But close collaboration between marketing, sales, manufacturing research and design is essential. To guarantee the delivery of defect-free products that meet customer requirements, systems must be created to continuously monitor markets and available technologies, and translate the results into specifications for manufacturing and design.

Mastering the circle

A more radical solution is possible, illustrated by Toyota's strategy. The flurry of new models and the Lexus venture into the traditional reserve of German speciality car producers demonstrates a company squaring the circle with a deep understanding of its manufacturing abilities. Its production system is based on a very sophisticated application of just-in-time concepts and total quality management, providing it with significant and recognised core manufacturing competencies. It is in a position to easily broaden its square. With a marginal investment in manufacturing capabilities, Toyota may be able to enlarge it significantly.

Especially if synergies can be gained from new manufacturing capabilities which reinforce existing strengths.

Adding new design change capabilities without lessening quality may offer exciting potential for quickly launching a series of new or varied products, without the teething problems that were expected and accepted in the past. This means that at some point, the square may become bigger than the circle. Then companies would no longer have to follow the elusive circle. Think of the excitement of kindly guiding the circle around your company's square. Or the pleasure of pushing your competitor's smaller square around.

Observers of consumer electronics markets must have wondered whether customers really needed three generations of hand-held camcorders each year, which is what Sony offered the year it introduced its passport format camcorder. What if Sony is simply pushing its competitors around, those whose manufacturing is not lithe enough for this 'dance' around the square?

Today's task is implementing mechanisms to follow the movements of the circle. Tomorrow's challenge lies in building and enforcing manufacturing capabilities in order to create squares with enough room to push less able competitors around.

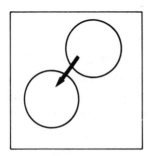

Figure 4.7 Pushing the competitor around

CREATING MOMENTUM

How to create and implement a good quality management programme can be found in other books. Below is a short checklist of the categories an improvement programme needs to address, based on the same categories used for the Malcolm Baldridge National Quality Award.

Leadership

Leadership includes both symbolic acts that stress the importance of the quality programme, and active involvement by the company's top managers. Some general communication programme is needed, with posters, slogans, and arguments explaining the need for quality. Putting quality issues on the agenda of each senior directors' meeting, or mentioning quality in every speech or informal interaction with the employees is essential to providing the employees with the motivation to surmount the daily challenges of operational and financial standards.

But communication has to be backed up with the active personal involvement of top leaders. Garvin describes how J. R. Houghton of Corning Glassworks analysed his own work schedule according to the Baldridge categories. He discovered that he spent 30 per cent of his value added time 'creating the appropriate environment and value system which stimulates the morale and productivity of the workforce and leadership'. This 'beating of the drum' motivated 40 or 50 visits each year to customers and to Corning locations, with the focus on progress towards world quality goals.[3]

Information and analysis

Knowing what customers want is the first step to squaring the circle. This kind of information must be easily accessible and be circulated throughout the company. Quality database systems used to promise a vast information system through which the

---

[3] Garvin, D., 1991, 'How the Baldridge Award Really Works', *Harvard Business Review*, Vol. 69, no. 6, pp. 80–95.

company could follow from headquarters the status of product defects, process performance, customer complaints or supplier quality. Calls for a comprehensive view of quality costs (or costs of non-quality, as they were called) were implicitly based on such centralised views.

Implementing strategic quality information systems requires that relevant information be accessible from all geographical, hierarchical or functional dimensions. A researcher in Tokyo must be able to access relevant data on market requirements in Spain or Indonesia. A salesperson in the US must be able to access production capacities available in Mexico. And the production manager in the UK should be able to benchmark his plant's production capabilities with colleagues or competitors in Italy, Sweden or Canada.

Strategic quality planning

A fairly limited set of concrete, focused, integrated and aggressive goals over a one to two-year period should exist. The company must be able to say explicitly and specifically what it is going to do and why. Companies often set goals which stretch current quality records, such as a ten or 100-fold improvement.

Since 1988, 'Management Today', a British publication, has annually selected Britain's best factories. Looking at the sample of 15 or 20 companies which have received the award over the years, few similarities are seen among their action plans. But without exception, all had achieved impressive improvements by stretching performance goals.

Human resource optimisation

Unleashing workforce potential is nothing new. But believing in people and giving them the means to solve problems is essential to quality management programmes.

In Philips' Tyne and Wear deflection unit plant in Washington, managers concluded in the mid-80s that among all the problems and challenges facing the plant, they had one major asset: the workforce. Largely unspecialised and not very highly educated employees were able to work faster and better than any of the company's Japanese rivals. But the workforce needed resources to carry out its tasks. Rather than automate the factory, management decided to rebuild the manufacturing process around employees. Selective automation leveraged their skills instead of replacing them. The results have been impressive. First-time yields increased from 72 per cent to 98 per cent in three years.

These are issues involving the selection of good people, effective training, and continuous motivation.

Quality assurance of products and services

Getting a good square requires understanding and learning about key processes. Obtaining a perfect square requires pursuing a profound understanding of support processes.

Quality results

Nothing is as motivating as obtaining and rewarding results. A successful quality programme needs a system to measure its results. What are the meaningful trends in the results obtained through quality programmes? How do results change over the years? How fast are results obtained?

Customer satisfaction

What evidence do we have that we understand the customer, and how quick are we in reacting to changing customer requirements or a changing customer base? How do we measure customer complaints, and how do we not see them as a problem but rather as an opportunity for improving customer satisfaction?

More complete checklists are available. The management issue is not developing exhaustive checklists, but creating the momentum to continuously update the checklist, and assisting efforts to square the circle. James Teboul used an image of 'priming the pump' – making sure that top management creates the right environment and organisational structure to 'pump up' quality problems. This means making them visible to the organisation; providing the energy to pump them through change-resistant filters, organisational inefficiencies or lack of know-how; keeping motivation high and finally measuring the results. The seven elements mentioned above may help create the momentum and keep the pump working.

SUMMARY

The three stages of quality management
1. Quality as Corrective Action.
2. Quality as Opportunity.
3. Strategic Quality Management.

Squaring the circle – matching capabilities with the market
Defining the Circle: the market requirements.
Managing the Square: the company's offering.
Mastering the Circle: managing the overlap between the two, or actively making your company's square larger than the circle.

Creating momentum
The following elements are the building blocks for strategic quality management:
- Leadership
- Information and Analysis
- Strategic Quality Planning
- Human Resources
- Quality Assurance of Products and Services
- Quality Results
- Customer Satisfaction.

5 THE NEW CHALLENGE – COST EFFICIENT FLEXIBILITY

What is the next objective for strategic manufacturing, once high quality is demoted from competitive advantage to basic necessity? For the past few years there have been suggestions that combining customisation and cost efficiency may be next.

The Audi 80 example in Chapter 2, illustrating the huge potential for variety, is not unique. The same drive to customise products is underway in other industries: a Japanese producer of mountain bikes can produce more than 11,000,000 versions of his product. The producers of Swatch watches can change product design almost daily. Creating this level of design flexibility is not necessarily the challenge. Artists and artisans do it all the time. The real challenge is doing it cost efficiently.

CHANGES IN THE FLEXIBILITY CHALLENGE

Flexibility is a manufacturing term which has been much used and even more misused. Simply defined, it is manufacturing's ability to adapt to change – any kind of change. Managing these flexible responses must be adapted to the specific nature of the change.

The source of change – endogenous or exogenous?

Classifying different types of flexibility is facilitated by thinking in two dimensions (Figure 5.1.) The first dimension is whether the change to which one is responding is *endogenous* or *exogenous*. In other words, whether it is inherent to the current system, or whether it is the result of unexpected, external change.

Short-term fluctuations in demand, labour strikes, shortfalls in deliveries, and breakdowns in machinery are endogenous, because they arise within the production system. Typical responses to such events involve building safety nets into the system, ranging from creating surplus stocks of incoming goods to providing some slack in capacity.

Exogenous events are external uncertainties related to unexpected moves by competitors, new technologies or new products. Back-up systems such as safety stocks cannot be built to cope with these. What is needed is alertness, reactivity and effective integration of the firm's different activities.

The response – operational vs. asset flexibility

The second dimension distinguishes between operational flexibility and asset flexibility. Operational flexibility refers to manufacturing responses to change which do not affect a company's fixed assets, systems or procedures. Asset flexibility is the ability to adapt capital equipment, human resources, manufacturing strategies or all the systems and procedures used in manufacturing.

Two of the quadrants in this matrix (1 and 4) represent familiar situations. It is common practice to respond to endogenous, or

	Operational flexibility	Asset flexibility
Endogenous changes	1 Safety stocks to cope with unreliable suppliers	2 Close down a factory to cope with reduction in demand
Exogenous changes	3 Flexible manufacturing system	4 Building a new factory on the occasion of a new product

Figure 5.1 Examples of manufacturing flexibility

internal, changes with operational flexibility. Unreliable suppliers, fluctuations in demand, or an unpredictable workforce are countered with a host of established safety measures. Exogenous, or external changes such as new product introductions or new technologies, often result in adapting asset structures.

In both cases, the primary issue is cost containment. The economically optimal level of safety stocks is carefully calculated. If a new factory is being envisaged for a new product, financial hurdle rates and minimising investment are usually guiding factors.

New challenges

The other two quadrants in the matrix (2 and 3) used to be considered areas to be avoided. Responding to endogenous changes such as shifts in market forecasts by adapting assets – through lay-offs or factory closures – was considered a failure. Answering exogenous change with existing operational resources was considered either impossible or extremely inefficient. Rapid introduction of a new product on an existing production line, for example, was rarely considered an option.

In the automobile industry, it used to be common for factories to shut down and be completely revamped over a period of weeks or months to prepare for the introduction of a new model. In the chemical industry, product and process were considered to be closely interwoven – anything other than a completely dedicated production line was considered irrational. In the rare cases where new products were run on existing lines, it was seen as a barely acceptable and very inefficient transition phase where the emphasis was on terminating it as quickly as possible.

Today's challenge is managing these two lesser-known quadrants more actively. Take the example of the introduction of a new product, an exogenous change (Quadrant 2). In many industries product life cycles are becoming shorter while in others, the very concept of a standardised product has been lost and all products are customised to satisfy the market. Companies simply cannot afford to build a new production line for every new product. Time constraints force companies to respond with operational flexibility. And inefficient solutions are unacceptable. Consequently, everyone is experimenting with Flexible Manufacturing Systems.

Allen Bradley's printed circuit board production lines are described in a Harvard Business School case.[1] Over a ten year period, the company's market for industrial devices changed drastically. From a playing field of half a dozen competitors with product life cycles of more than ten years, Allen Bradley suddenly found itself surrounded by over 150 competitors and product life cycles which narrowed to a window of market opportunity of about two years.

Once upon a time, Allen Bradley could react to a competitor's product at its own pace, producing the new products on dedicated assembly lines. Now, it is forced to design and introduce the new product quickly, on existing production lines, in volumes which would have been considered inefficiently low only a decade ago.

That leaves the other uninviting quadrant, number 3. Fast asset flexibility has always been considered a contradiction in terms. Almost by definition, companies do not like to adapt their assets quickly. Yet that may be what is now required. As markets become more volatile, the pace of technological obsolescence quickens, and in some cases raw material alternatives become more viable (for example, switching from steel to plastic screws). So the degree of flexibility of investments in plant and machinery, human resources or information systems may need to be re-evaluated.

Television sets are a mass-produced item, with limited possibilities for differentiation. Common sense suggests manufacturing such a product on dedicated production lines, run close to capacity. The ideal would be to produce constant, stable output, with minimal variation. Yet, in Europe, the television set market is cyclical. More televisions are sold in autumn than in spring. To cope, television producers tended to build up inventories during the first six months of the year – a response typical of operational flexibility.

---

[1] Allen Bradley: 'Electronic Manufacturing Strategy', 1990, *Harvard Business School*, Case no. 9–161–018

Toshiba took a more creative approach in its UK factory. It established an agreement with its labour force: fewer hours would be worked in the first half of the year, while more hours would be put in in the second half. On average, the number of hours worked remained unchanged, but Toshiba created some asset flexibility (in human resource costs) to respond to expected market fluctuations. This enabled Toshiba to follow market demand more closely, without incurring inventory holding costs.

Integration and co-ordination are key

Why are these new areas of flexibility so difficult to manage? First, because of an evolution in emphasis. Traditional management of the first and the fourth quadrant was based on cost containment. Safety stocks were optimised, forecasting systems were fine-tuned, and automation was concerned with labour-input reductions and hardware integration. Actions identified with the second or the third quadrant were tolerated only if pure reaction speed was imperative.

If this type of action becomes more common, companies will be forced to guarantee not only cost containment but reaction speed as well. And they are not used to it. In fact, companies implicitly expect faster reaction speeds to result in higher costs. Yet the message promoted by publications specialised in time-based competition is that this correlation can be reversed.

The second source of difficulty is the systemic nature of flexibility. A system becomes more flexible only if every element of the system increases and exploits its flexibility. This is how it differs from cost considerations, because the total cost of a system can fall as soon as the cost of any one element of the system decreases.

Assume that a company has a simple production system (consisting of a series of production and assembly steps) and a distribution system. If cost efficiency can be improved in the production of one component, we end up with a lower overall cost (assuming it is a real cost improvement, and not a cost reallocation to another production step). The whole benefits from an improvement in a single element.

But flexibility has its own accounting. If one production phase installs a flexible manufacturing system, this does not guarantee that the whole chain becomes more flexible. All the other steps in the production process have to adapt to take advantage of the new flexibility.

A leading European manufacturer of speciality glass products invested heavily in a flexible, computer-integrated manufacturing system for polishing raw glass products. This change promised a reduction in manufacturing lead times – to be reduced from months to weeks.

But a lack of integration and co-ordination meant that the opportunity of offering drastically reduced manufacturing lead times was poorly communicated to the sales force and the distribution network. The sales force, distrusting manufacturing's new capabilities, did not use shorter delivery times in their sales arguments.

Distribution, always under time pressure to deliver and install the products, welcomed the shorter manufacturing lead times to increase its own lead time. Only after top management asked some pointed questions about the final return on the CIM project – some two years after its implementation – did the company realise the extent of the opportunities it had lost. Had the CIM project concentrated on cost savings, the result would probably have trickled immediately down to the bottom line. The advantage of flexibility was only obtained once the whole value chain was made aware of it and exploited it actively.

How can the negative correlation between time reduction and cost improvements be broken? And what does this imply for the management of integration and co-ordination? The rest of the chapter seeks to answer these questions with a specific example: the increasing speed of design change and new product introductions. First, by showing how shortening design cycles can contribute to increasing the profitability of a new product, and then by suggesting how the process can be managed.

LINKING PROFITABILITY AND SHORTER DESIGN CYCLES

A simple model demonstrates how better time management during the development and manufacturing start-up phases of a new product can contribute to higher profitability over the product's life cycle.

Figure 5.2 shows a simplified evolution of the cumulative cash flow and sales over the life cycle of a product, from the first flash of a design idea to its withdrawal from the market. In the beginning, there are only negative cash flows, reflecting expenditures for research, development, manufacturing start-up and, for consumer products, the organisation of distribution channels. Cumulative cash flow becomes increasingly negative until the time of entry introduction (indicated by entry, when sales take off. Ideally, sales then grow, positive cash flows become greater than negative ones and the cumulative cash flow curve starts to rise. If sales stagnate or drop, the company withdraws the product from the market, hopefully after getting the overall cumulative cash flow to positive levels.

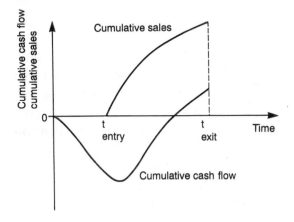

Figure 5.2 Cumulative cash flow and sales versus time

Timing product introductions and withdrawals

Who or what determines the timing of a product's withdrawal from the market? Customers who no longer want to buy the product? Competitors who launch a better product? The government which stops sales for safety reasons? Any or a combination of these conditions is decisive – the moment is determined by the market, or by the interaction of a variety of market forces.

Who or what determines the timing of a product introduction? It may seem, at first glance, that marketing should be responsible. In the case of very important projects, top management may have to be involved. But it is somewhat more complex. The timing of a product's introduction is often determined by its availability. That, in turn, is the result of development and manufacturing start-up. The actual moment of introduction is often determined by design, development, engineering and manufacturing.

If these groups are late, sales will start late. But that does not make them last any longer. So the company loses in terms of cumulative sales. The lost sales are those that would have been generated at the beginning of the product's life cycle. Without it being a law of nature, in more than 80 per cent of cases, sales in the first stages of product life cycles provide higher margins. So a

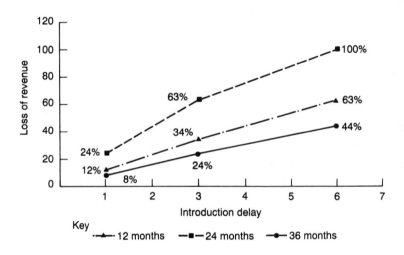

Figure 5.3 The impact of delay

double impact is created. Not only are sales lost, in absolute terms, but these losses are the most profitable. A small delay in introducing a product, therefore, can have a more than proportional impact on overall profit margins.

One US-based producer of electronic components made the following calculation. If the introduction of a product with a product life cycle of 12, 24 or 36 months, is delayed by one month, revenue losses amount to eight, 12 or 24 per cent, respectively, over the product's life cycle (Figure 5.3). A six month delay incurs losses of 100, 63 and 44 per cent, respectively. A delay equal to a sixth the length of the product's life cycle leads to revenues being halved. Enough reasons to pay attention to timely product introductions.

Overlapping development cycles

Being on time does not necessarily imply shorter development cycles. In fact, it would suffice to start early and improve the control over the time required between a product idea's first formulation through to its introduction. Take a company that needs two years to develop a new video recorder. Marketing has decided to introduce the product at a specific date. The company can start development two years earlier, assuming it sticks to schedule.

It may actually be advantageous to do more than simply control a long development time. It may be better to actually reduce the length of the development cycle. Figure 5.4 shows why.

The moment a product is withdrawn from the market, companies ideally have a replacement ready. The development of the replacement should have started months or years earlier. Figure 5.4 suggests that if we do not shorten development times, the replacement product may have been in development even before the first product was ever introduced. That implies that the two products, both aimed at the same market but with introductions at different times, are developed in parallel. That leads to trouble – for both the marketing and the technical sides of the company.

What will be the first product manager's reaction when he sees

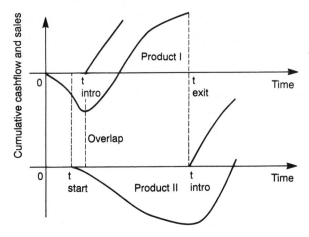

Figure 5.4 Cumulative cash flows versus time with two products

that a new product is in development, complete with attractive new options? He will yearn to include at least some of them in his product. This is likely to cause a delay in the introduction of the first product, making overall profitability decrease.

This overlap also creates difficulties for the technical side of the company. Companies usually have only a few experts specialised in the specific aspects of development of two products aimed at the same market. They will be forced to divide their time and attention between several products – guaranteeing the inefficient use of their talents.

Does such an overlap actually occur? A low end video recorder has a life cycle of about six months. During the second half of the 1980s, development and start-up took a major European VCR producer between 18 and 21 months. The company had between three and four models under development simultaneously. A leading Far Eastern producer boasted that it needed only four or five months. It had drastically simplified both the development and the product launch. It had only one product aimed at a given market segment under development at any given time. It was also able to fine-tune the choice of the launch date because development time was one to two months shorter than the product's normal life cycle.

Working this reasoning to its conclusion, the development of a new product should not start before the previous product aimed at the same market has been safely launched. That provides an upper limit for the time needed to develop a product. Yet companies continue to try to shorten product development times. The Far Eastern VCR producer strives for a development time of four months. Honda has shortened the development time for its cars well beyond the four years it wants between introductions of two similar types of car. Why?

Some companies want to incorporate market data about previous products in the design of new products. In other cases they want to use the latest technology. The main reason seems to be that companies want to limit the amount of forecasting involved. The closer the development phase is to the date of introduction, the less guesswork there will be about what the market really wants or that new technologies actually allow.

MANAGING THE PROCESS

Attacking wasted time in development cycles

What can be done to reduce wasted time during the development and start up of new products? The answer does not lie in speeding up the execution of technical tasks. In developing a new product, all the components must be developed to guarantee product integrity. Cutting corners in technical development is not likely to contribute to success in the market.

It is in the interfaces that the slack is to be found: between the different functions in the company and between the various steps in the development and start up process. The interaction between groups and the transfer processes between design, product and process development, and production is where valuable time is lost.

Three areas in particular merit attention. This is not an exhaustive summary of everything that can be done to shorten design cycle times. But it is a start to improving time performance. First, the whole development and start up process needs to be cleaned up. Secondly, technical tasks can, under certain conditions, be carried out in parallel. And thirdly, a systemic approach can be tremendously helpful in shortening cycles.

Cleaning up development and start up

In a worldwide study of textile loom producers carried out by the author, two attitudes to product development and manufacturing start up (Figure 5.5) were observed.

This graph defines the development phase as a process of uncertainty reduction. When it begins, there are many unresolved questions about product and process design. Ideally, they would all be answered by the time the product is introduced. With *strategy A*, the company defines all the specifications up front, in minute detail, and goes through an almost painful process of exploring feasible alternatives. This is a highly integrated approach involving all the different functional groups. Once everything is finalised, these companies go ahead with development and manufacturing start up. The specifications are considered to be set in stone and changes, at least in theory, are unthinkable.

Strategy B aims at keeping all the options open. A lot of technical work is carried out within separate functional departments, processes are installed, contacts with suppliers are made, etc., but

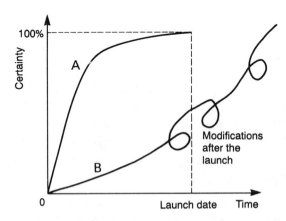

Figure 5.5 Two types of planning

these companies refuse to commit themselves to specifications. They aim to remain flexible in order to be able to react to unforeseen changes in the market. Once they get close to the planned date of introduction they believe that all the preparatory work will allow them to put the product together quickly, according to the latest specifications.

Both strategies seem to have their strong points. But strategy B has a major drawback – it is almost impossible to implement. Rarely can a company pull together all the technical answers needed to live up to the latest specifications. And as the figure suggests, development lingers on, so that when the date of introduction finally approaches, the company is faced with an impossible choice: postponing the introduction or launching a product that will require a lot of subsequent engineering changes.

The message is clear: invest heavily up front in the definition of specifications, and stick to it. And organise so that the company is able to live with the selected approach. It may require an excellent database of alternative solutions and techniques; good simulation programmes for testing hypotheses and designs; even postponing prototype construction until a company knows what it wants. But even more important is creating integrated organisations where manufacturers, developers and markets can meet, discuss and determine specifications they can abide by during the development phase. The greatest challenge is sticking to this discipline during the development and manufacturing start up.

Parallel development and engineering

Time can be saved on the execution of technical tasks. Things can also be more timely and effective in the transfer of design specifications from one department (design) to another (manufacturing), and in solving problems between departments and functions. In their seminal study of the world's automobile industry, Kim Clark and Takeo Fujimoto[2] stress the importance of

---

[2] Clark K.B. and Fujimoto T.,1991, *Product Development Performance, Strategy, Organisation and Management in the World Auto Industry*, Harvard Business School Press, Boston.

simultaneous engineering as a way of reducing development and manufacturing start-up times.

The principle is simple: tasks which are normally carried out sequentially are executed in parallel. This typically involves product and process engineering. Traditional approaches would have argued that product development and engineering come first. Once the product specifications had been determined, the design and engineering of the production process could start. But when saving time becomes management's main goal, it is tempting to carry out product and process engineering in parallel. Such methods were used during World War II for developing military material, but were later abandoned for being too messy and not meeting standards of scientific management. They have recently been rediscovered in both the electronics and the automobile industry.

Although the principle is simple, its implementation is not. Companies are familiar with how to solve problems in either product or process engineering. But how do they solve problems with an impact on both? How is a simple problem solved, such as the positioning of a screw? One position optimises the product's mechanical strength but defies assembly by a robot. Another position puts the mechanical strength at risk, but allows highly automated production. A trivial example perhaps, but typical of the design problems of numerous durable consumer products.

In a sequential world, these issues do not pose a problem. Product engineers design, and process engineers adapt themselves to the result. But how do companies organise themselves for these tasks to be carried out in parallel? Do product engineers have complete freedom, and are process engineers surprised in the middle of their design efforts with the results of their colleagues' creative efforts? Should some form of binding information exchange be established, putting the process engineers in a reactive mode vis-a-vis the product engineers? Or should they solve problems together? If the latter is given preference, the resulting implementation difficulties must be clearly understood. A somewhat artificial example illustrates them.

Everyone has had the experience of being stuck in a traffic jam in a big city. A long line of cars waits at a red light to get across an intersection. When the light turns green, the first car accelerates, and only once it has left does the second car start forward. Only then does the third car accelerate, and so on. By the time the fifth car gets its turn, the light is red again. Ideally, everyone should start off simultaneously when the light first turns green, with the same rate of acceleration. Many more cars would make it across the intersection during the short interval that the light is green. But no one dares.

That is exactly what simultaneous engineering is about. The standard approach, queuing up in front of a red light, symbolises sequential engineering. Doing it in parallel, with every car accelerating at the same time is simultaneous engineering. Doing it without information exchange can lead to unpleasant surprises, or even confusion: which is what happens if process engineering remains in a reactive mode. Information exchange can help. That is what honking is for: it stimulates the driver in front to take off at the same moment.

The example is somewhat simplistic, but it illustrates a number of the conditions necessary to make simultaneous engineering work. First and foremost, it requires clear procedures (when to take off and at what rate of acceleration). It implies trusting the other party to solve their part of the problem within the boundaries of the procedures that were established jointly. And communication must be possible with the other party as soon as a problem arises. If a car has a foreign licence plate, it may need to be called to check whether it is familiar with established procedures. That assumes that there is a telephone in the car, that the number is displayed on the rear window and that one is willing to take into account the other car driver's potential problems. In manufacturing terms, it means being able to quickly detect problems, contact the other departments involved and solve the problem directly.

The major difficulty in implementing simultaneous engineering (or similar techniques carrying a different name, such as parallel or concurrent engineering), observed in companies such as Ford of Europe or British Aerospace, is recognising and solving problems at lower management levels. Currently, systems do not exist for assisting professional employees at lower levels in the organisation in detecting problems and sharing and solving them with their colleagues in other departments.

A systemic approach to development and start up

The third recommendation is the organisational leverage effect of innovation. The principle is simple. If a company innovates, and its innovation is successful, there will always be others who benefit. Component suppliers may see an increase in the demand for their products, customers may see your products as potential boosts to their productivity, and universities may discover a source of ideas for publications. If all these different players benefit from the innovation, they may as well carry some of its burden. In other words, can a company use future benefits as a carrot to leverage their capabilities to solve some current problems?

In the same study of the world's automobile industry referred to earlier, the authors came to the conclusion that some of the fast developers made extensive use of a network of suppliers and subcontractors to develop 'black box' parts. These are parts for which the boundary constraints are well defined, but sub-contractors are given the freedom to develop them (Table 5.1).

A similar process can be observed in the development of photo-copiers. A Japanese producer of low end copiers explained that for some models, the company only developed 10 or 15 per cent of the product. The rest was developed by a selection of subcontractors. When these subcontractors were asked how they developed their

Type of supplier as percentage of total purchased parts	North American producers	Japanese producers	European producers
proprietary parts	3	8	7
black box parts	16	62	39
detail controlled parts	81	30	54

Source: Clark and Fujimoto, 1991

Table 5.1 Proportion of different types of suppliers

share of the product, they responded: 'Well we develop about 15 per cent, the rest is developed by our suppliers.' It turned out that the manufacturer's supplier/developer network was five levels deep. Some minor plastic or mechanical components were developed by small companies five levels away from the 'producing' company.

Working in such an environment does not guarantee speed of development. Yet if the fourth or fifth level of the development network is a small entrepreneurial company with two machines, ten employees, and a simple desk-top CAD system, the potential may exist to react faster than a German competitor whose design workforce has a 36 hour week. But the potential advantage of speed may be offset by the complexity of the supplier network.

In order to manage such a network well, three conditions must be fulfilled.

1. Development and manufacturing management must become project and network management rather than the traditional repetitive manufacturing.
2. Co-ordination through mutual adjustment within the network needs to be established. What one supplier designs may have an impact on what another supplier produces. A supplier network reflex of looking at what others need and offer needs to be created, overcoming the reflex of local optimisation.
3. It must be accepted that not all design details and constraints are communicated in formal ways. Instead, perhaps this can be replaced by an atmosphere of belonging to a club, without overly detailed design rules and objectives.

When Toyota opened two factories in the UK, the company went through a very detailed and long-winded procedure to select its suppliers. A French automobile supplier described how after having 'applied', it had taken Toyota more than a year to evaluate its capabilities. Not only was the supplier's technology analysed from top to bottom, but so were its production processes, equipment, cycle times and organisation. Though such an evaluation has obvious technical objectives, it also serves to indoctrinate the potential supplier with 'the Toyota way'.

DELAYED DIFFERENTIATION: AN ALTERNATIVE TO FAST NEW PRODUCT DEVELOPMENT

New products do not always need to be customised from the initial concept. The new product development ideas developed in this chapter are simply one way of satisfying customers. An alternative is to build products with multiple components which can be combined in thousands of ways. The basic idea is that product customisation be postponed until the last step in the production process.

Many companies already do. Benetton postpones dyeing its clothes until the last minute of the production process. A major European industrial pizza producer makes standardised pizzas, but adds different flavours and spices just before final packaging in order to cater to differences in customer taste between Northern and Southern Europe.

Hewlett Packard's production of laser printers for global markets serves as an example. Each market has different electrical standards with different plugs, voltages and frequencies. With a simple design, the electric cable can be produced with a standardised connecter which connects to the printer. This allows Hewlett Packard to produce standard laser printers which can be used worldwide. By adding a package with a locally adapted electric cable and a manual, printers are easily customised for specific markets. The standard product is produced at high volumes in a single factory in Vancouver, and customisation is done in the distribution warehouses of each country. In addition to offering cheaper automatisation, such an approach also leads to shorter reaction times. Specific customer requests do not require changes in production, just a simple manipulation of plugs in the local distribution warehouse.

Every example demonstrates the same process: automation is combined with cost efficient component production, by postponing customisation to the last stages of production. This may sound simple, but it requires a totally different approach to product design. Dyeing clothes at the last moment, or designing printers with an easy-to-connect cable is neither the cheapest nor the most effective solution for product design! It requires a totally different attitude from both the design and the manufacturing department. Product, process and factory lay-out all have to be adapted to 'postpone' differentiation. But the benefits can be high. This delayed differentiation allows companies to respond to specific customer requests without having to redesign products.

SUMMARY

Adapting to change
- defining the origin of change
- endogenous (inherent to current system)
- exogenous (external, unexpected)
- selecting the type of response
- operational flexibility
- asset flexibility
- managing new responses – working with the lesser-known quadrants of the model, flexible manufacturing systems and asset flexibility.

Two keys to flexibility: integration and co-ordination. The whole is only as flexible as the sum of the flexibility of the parts.

Profitability through shorter design cycles
The levers of shortening design cycles:
- the timing of product introductions and withdrawals
- making development cycles overlap.

Managing the process means:
- attacking wasted time in development cycles
- cleaning up development and start up
- running development and engineering tasks in parallel
- establishing systemic approaches to development and start up.

Delayed differentiation can be an alternative to fast new product development.

6 BEYOND QUALITY & FLEXIBILITY – THE INTEGRATED FACTORY

Introducing flexibility and managing quality depends on the successful integration of the manufacturing function into the organisation as a whole. It has to work in synergy with other functions such as sales, purchasing or engineering. But flexibility and quality do not depend solely on internal factors. They are strongly affected by external considerations. So any effort at integration must take into account the company's external partners – suppliers, customers and the environment.

A MANUFACTURING CARICATURE

In the 1960s and 1970s, manufacturing functions often attempted to work in splendid isolation. The result can be described with an exaggerated representation of the manufacturing function (Figure 6.1). The figure shows how manufacturing buffered itself from its environment, with six of the most common hedges against the outside world.[1]

Manufacturing preferred behaving as if individual employees did not exist. Their involvement, therefore, was rendered unnecessary, and work force management simply involved managing the relationship between management and the unions.

For many manufacturers, customers were also an abstract concept. What really mattered were forecasts, sales representatives,

[1] see De Meyer, A. and Ferdows, K., 1992, Removing the Barriers in Manufacturing, in Miller, J.G., De Meyer, A. and Nakane, J., *Benchmarking Global Manufacturing*, Business One Irwin, Homewood Illinois.

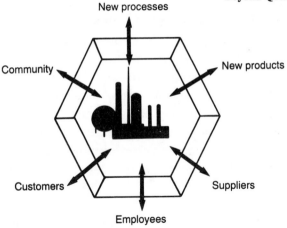

Figure 6.1 The integrated factory

materials requirements planning systems and master schedule plans.

New products were considered necessary, but their introduction was an unwelcome disruption of smooth production flows and a drag on factory efficiency. If they had to be introduced, engineering was expected to ensure that all the specifications were as detailed and precise as possible. It was not that surprises were not appreciated – they were simply not allowed.

Suppliers were, almost by definition, unreliable. Likely to be late, they provided low quality components delivered in the wrong quantities. In order to be protected from such reliable unreliability, factories created protective mountains of inventories and imposed strict quality control procedures on suppliers.

New processes were tolerated, perforce. But financial hurdle rates were often set so high that any investment that made it over the barriers of scrutiny and evaluation was bound to be conservative. No room was made for experimenting with new production methods or state of the art technologies.

The factory's environment was unquestioningly ignored. Environmentalism and product life cycle responsibility were concepts yet to be conceived, at least as far as manufacturing was concerned. Rare was the company that took a proactive approach towards the demands of any movement tinted green. Most, if not all, manufacturers obediently applied government imposed rules and procedures. But any further foray into environmental management was seen as incomprehensible overspending. Although audits measuring the impact of a company on its environment were quite popular during the latter half of the 60s, and the first years of the 70s, they quickly disappeared when the second oil crisis hit, and with the advent of Reaganomics. With a few exceptions, they proved to be mere public relations exercises.

Caricatures cost money

Such extremist attitudes are caricatures. No manufacturing organisation was ever quite this exaggerated. But most factories revealed some of these characteristics – and many still do. There are obvious reasons for so much buffering. By limiting the influence of external forces, it becomes a lot easier to optimise what goes on inside the factory. Any mathematically based method becomes much simpler when boundary conditions are stable. Factory managers were quick to understand this and tried to contain the uncontainable.

These buffers hid huge disadvantages. Most of them either proved costly or served to slow reaction speeds. Inventories increase the need for working capital and limit alternative investment opportunities. Filters between labour and management disrupt communication flows, preventing good ideas from being brought to management's attention, and reducing active problem solving on the factory floor. Late implementation of good employee ideas can be an expensive lapse.

Lack of attention to a factory's environmental impact – a cheap short-term solution – can lead to astronomical costs the day the accumulated damage has to be cleaned up. By resisting the inevitable trend towards more environmentally friendly processes, companies miss market opportunities to sell innovative approaches to competitors.

Nippon Steel and Ciba Geigy are two companies showing the way. In 1987, Nippon Steel emitted 75 per cent less nitrogen oxide and 90 per cent less dust than it did in 1970. For one ton of amide,

Ciba Geigy used to use three tons of highly corrosive 'phosphore trichlorate' and 12 tons of water, producing 14 tons of effluents that had to be treated. That process has been replaced by one that uses only 1.9 tons of raw materials and no water at all. The by-products of the new process can easily be recycled or burnt. By taking a proactive attitude towards the environment, these companies have developed leading processes. They can eventually offer licences to some of their competitors, thereby reaping the benefits of the process as well as the royalties of the licensing agreements.

Buffers between development and production, or hurdles imposed on process investments, drastically slow reaction speed, and limit the learning curve that accompanies continuous product and process experimentation. Working with forecasts rather than with real customer demand data guarantees piling up inventories of unsold goods, unadapted to customer needs.

BREAKING DOWN BUFFERS

The last decade has witnessed companies breaking down these types of barriers. Just-in-time programmes have been implemented to get rid of mountainous inventories. Lead times have been reduced, limiting the need for forecasts.

Factories are in the process of removing the barriers with which they surrounded themselves. The next challenge is integration with other functions – internally with marketing, development and process engineering; externally with suppliers, customers and the local community. The whole notion of manufacturing function as a separate entity needs to be forgotten. It no longer works. Manufacturing is not one step in a linear process bringing a piece of defined hardware to customers. It is becoming an integral part of one, long value-creating chain.

Suppliers as partners

Integration with suppliers is becoming fashionable. Intelligent manufacturers have discovered that, rather than treat suppliers as adversaries, it pays to make them partners. Suppliers should be selected on their willingness to form partnerships for tomorrow – not on their ability to offer the lowest price today. Previous chapters described the role that suppliers can play in the development of new products. But this implies a long-term collaborative approach to create a relation of trust. Trust is what transforms suppliers of goods into design partners and generators of ideas. Creating such partnerships is not easy. It often requires shared investments and a willingness by the main contractor to see suppliers through difficult periods.

Citroën, a part of the French automobile group PSA, invested a great deal of effort in establishing a set of suppliers for its factory in Rennes. They are required to work within the context of a just-in-time delivery process. The strategy has been successful and the number of suppliers within a 100 km radius of Rennes has doubled between 1986 and 1991. Twelve automotive suppliers have built factories near Rennes. Subcontracting increased by 40 per cent in volume, while the number of employees in the Rennes factory was reduced by over 10 per cent.

When sales of Citroën's top model, the XM did not reach expected sales targets, the company carefully managed the repercussions this could have on certain of their subcontractors. For some, the loss of sales was compensated by sales of components for other models, usually produced in the Paris region. Other automotive suppliers were invited to participate actively in the design of the replacement of the future mid-range model. Citroën's commitment to its supplier partnership policy has convinced other automotive suppliers to make sizeable investments in the Rennes region, even in difficult economic times.

Partnerships with suppliers is not a new idea. It has been in existence in the US and Europe for a long time. But its relevance for the effectiveness of a production system has been newly emphasised following studies of Japanese factories. Cusumano and Takeishi[2] raise this point in a study of supplier relationships in the automobile industry. They observed that, compared with US companies, the Japanese had lower levels of vertical integration and more affiliated supplier companies. They also had fewer suppliers per part, longer supplier contracts, elaborate systems which force decreasing prices, extremely low and improving defect rates, and high levels of information exchange with suppliers, including frequent supplier suggestions for improvement.

In choosing suppliers, Japanese companies, somewhat surprisingly, place the greatest emphasis on price. Since relationships are clearly long-term, survey respondents may not have wanted to single out business relationships as a selection factor. This example may instead illustrate that partnerships with suppliers do not exclude challenging cost improvement objectives.

The Japanese approach to supplier relationships may be a consequence of the country's industrial history, which after the World War II was heavily concentrated on catching up. Such an effort favoured the technical specialisation of individual firms and led naturally to partnerships and collaborative efforts.

The same approach seems to be relatively easy to transplant elsewhere. Transplants of the Japanese automobile industry in the US have many similar characteristics regarding supplier relations. US industry as a whole has moved closer to what could be considered a more Japanese approach to supplier management. The Japanese transplants in the US have proved their worth as leaders in terms of quality improvement rates. They also had the fewest suppliers per part and, when introducing a new car, selected suppliers at the earliest stage of the process.

Environmental strategies

Another barrier to fall is lackadaisical attitudes towards the environment. Ecology has entered the factory. Manufacturing companies now proactively integrate environmental considera-

---

[2] Cusumano, M.A. and Takeishi, A., 1991, 'Supplier Relationship and Management: A Survey of Japanese, Japanese-Transplant and US Auto Plants', *Strategic Management Journal*, Vol. 12, pp. 563–588.

tions into their business strategies. A 1990 survey conducted among 600 managers by the German ministry of the environment, showed that 86 per cent of them have an environmental strategy aimed both at reducing costs and at capturing new markets.

Since 1986, Rhône Poulenc, the French chemical giant, has invested large sums to restructure chemical waste. The company no longer knew how to treat the enormous amounts of waste produced by its factories. What at first seemed a reactive strategy quickly became a proactive attack on the sources of chemical waste. It turned out to be a profitable investment in installing clean technologies as early in the process stream as possible.

By motivating its engineering teams to eliminate chemical waste, Rhône Poulenc has been able to reduce costs of raw materials, transport and energy. A FF 60 million investment to treat effluent water in the production process of nylon yielded about FF 20 million in returns per year. It also led the company to develop new products and processes with which to conquer new markets. Another company, Air Liquide, estimates that 20 per cent of its growth over the next five to ten years will be due to activities which are derived from the replacement of toxic gases such as Freon by environmentally friendly products.

Even more acute, companies that have proved slow in evolving towards environmentally friendly products and processes may have won one battle with governments or environmental groups in the short term. But they may have lost a longer term war if corporate image suffers irrecoverable damage affecting future market share. A clear example involved recoverable packaging companies in Germany. The companies which resisted recycling legislation lost the legal battle, and in addition had to pay a levy on their products. Companies which had proactively created partnerships to collect glass, aluminium or other packaging materials, quickly recovered their initial investments through dramatic increases in market share.

The conclusion is unavoidable: let the environment enter the factory by taking a proactive environmental stance. It pays off. Companies have recognised this and are now following BMW in starting research and development in the area of the 'manufacturability of disposability' – how to design products so that the components can easily be disposed of after use. Current advertisements for German automobile manufacturers such as BMW, Opel or Volkswagen which announces the proportion of components that can be recycled probably marks the beginning of a very important trend.

Experimenting with new processes

New processes have always found their way into manufacturing. The latest machinery, robots, material handling systems or chemical process technologies are always adopted . . . eventually. New management systems such as Materials Requirements Planning (MRP I) or Manufacturing Resource Planning (MRP II), Just in Time, Statistical Process Control, Design for Manufacture or Quality Function Deployment (QFD) are the most recent examples.

In many cases, however, the introduction of new equipment or systems hinges on financial analyses. Return on investment is often difficult to calculate when something is new and experimental. Yet financial hurdle rates are often the most difficult obstacle to new investments being made. Future manufacturing strategies, learning in manufacturing or demonstrating the viability of particular technologies or systems are issues which are seldom addressed.

Opening the factory to new approaches requires a very different attitude. Where did ideas like JIT, SPC, CIM, or DFM originate? Not from the minds of illuminated researchers. These systems or technologies result from long processes of small, logical increments. Toyota's Ohno did not develop the Kanban system in a day. It and other Just-In-Time systems were built on lengthy and circuitous efforts driven by capital shortages and the imperative of catching up with top Western competitors.

Each day should mark a small step in improving manufacturing systems. Some will lead in the right direction; others will not. Both are necessary. No one knows exactly what the future benefits of these new approaches may be. Everyone suspects they exist, but experimentation is needed to find out what they are, and how they can best be obtained.

Some companies will take a wait-and-see attitude based on conservative attitudes driven by imposing financial hurdles and the difficulties of calculating highly uncertain rates of return. Their competitors are likely to be first in establishing future norms of world class manufacturing.

Another option is leadership, and that requires experimentation. Ten improvement projects need to be launched so that three or four can succeed. Such experiments impose some slack in production systems. This does not mean production systems need to be run inefficiently. But if the current production level is at 90 per cent of capacity – designed in the most efficient way currently conceivable – 10 per cent should be reserved for experimentation. Using such slack for learning about new processes is the sign of tomorrow's leaders in the manufacturing field.

Empowering people

Manufacturing must reach out to individual employees and stop depending entirely on traditional management / work force relations via the unions. Not that the value of unions in managing the labour force should be underestimated. In many European countries, unions are extremely valuable partners. But empowering employees is a strong trend in business today. Companies are pushing responsibility and decision making down to the lowest possible level in the organisation. So manufacturing organisations need to be prepared to work with new kinds of structures. They will emphasise flat hierarchies, human scale, individual initiative, small entrepreneurial units of about 100 employees, and sustained programmes of formal and informal training.

Since 1989, Rhône Poulenc has introduced a major drive to empower employees. The objective is for all units to organise themselves around the customer, a significant departure from the company's traditional functional organisation. One result is a totally new structure at the Saint-Fons Chimie manufacturing site, one of the group's original plants. The production department was scrapped, along with engineering, methods, maintenance and the human resource division. They were replaced with units of 150 to 200 employees. Some hierarchical levels were eliminated, and employees organised into semi-autonomous teams. The reorganisation created a more flexible, horizontal organisation oriented to customer needs.

Fortune Magazine called such self-managed teams 'the productivity breakthrough of the 1990s'.[3] They quote J. Houghton, CEO of Corning Glassworks, whose company has 3,000 teams, saying that 'if you really believe in quality, when you cut through everything, it's empowering your people; and it's empowering your people that leads to teams.'

Product development and production

Adversarial relations between manufacturing and product development deeply disrupt the production of an essential element of corporate survival: new products. Design for manufacturability, and free, two-way communication are absolutely necessary for the fast and effective introduction of new products. BMW has come to the conclusion that production quality and productivity are largely determined by a car's design and development process. So BMW has invested more than DM 1.5 billion in a revolutionary technical centre, begun in 1990. It will be fully operational in 1993 and bring together researchers, engineering quality managers, procurement and materials handling. All the parties involved in the development of a car will be united at a single site.

In addition to physically associating different parts of the process in a single location, BMW has completely changed the organisation of the development teams. Modular, multi-functional teams are established around a core group of ten to 15 people. They include design manufacturing, marketing and after-sales service engineers, and replace previous, more functional structures. About 30 or 40 of these teams work simultaneously on a new model. A team 'spokesperson' coordinates progress with the project manager. This integrated approach is even translated into the

---

[3] Dumaine, B., 1990, 'Who Needs a Boss?', *Fortune Magazine*, May 7, 1990, pp. 40–48.

company's architecture: buildings are modular, offices can be easily adapted, and walls moved to adapt to the needs of the teams.

Integrating the customer

Of prime importance is that the factory removes barriers between it and the customer. Too many systems and procedures are designed to guess what the customer needs. Rather than groping around for a benchmark 'customer' via forecasts and surveys, customers should be let in through the factory's front door and welcomed into the heart of production groups. Customers can also be invited to interact directly with production planning.

Some registration systems in France allow consumers to place orders through the local videotex system (Minitel). It is directly linked to the company's distribution scheduling system, which, in turn, hooks into the production system. Through a few information system filters, customers directly influence the production schedule. Companies can also use other valuable customer information to adapt production process. An office furniture manufacturer in Alsace-Lorraine invites its distributors' buyers to see for themselves how a particular desk or filing system is produced. Originally designed as a promotional tool for the company's quality procedures, it quickly became an extremely valuable source of information for the manufacturer. Customers suggested invaluable design and production improvements which ended up greatly facilitating the transport and assembly of the furniture on site.

MANAGING THE OPEN FACTORY

The factory described in Figure 6.1 does not work. It has to open up and work with other functions in the company and partners in its relevant environment. This may seem a daunting task for who is to manage this kind of factory? The old isolated factory was easily managed by a technical specialist with a sprinkling of people management skills. Boundary conditions were stable and production managers could concentrate on optimising the technological and human resources within them. That was the heyday of operations research techniques applied to production. Today, production managers have to do all that but much more as well. In addition to being proven technical specialists and good people managers, they also must be excellent diplomats who can build partnerships, and develop strong and innovative forms of collaboration.

Where will these managers come from? They are already in the organisation. They are the young engineers or business school graduates who have a specialised operational function. They will be the ones managing the open factory five years from now. But today is when career plans, training programmes, job rotation and exposure to different tasks must be included in their development. It is extremely important that tomorrow's needs be prepared for today. This development depends on good career planning, focusing on both individual and corporate requirements.

How fast can factories change?

This chapter ends with a word of caution. Throwing open the factory to outside influences and making it live in synergy with its partners in business is an intellectually attractive idea. In practice, it is extremely difficult to manage. Who can manage it? How fast can the process go? Too much speed and an unbalanced process of opening up the factory leads to instability. Turning walls and buffers into areas of interaction and collaboration has to be done gradually, and on all fronts simultaneously. Customers, suppliers, product development, process capabilities, employees and the environment have to be integrated simultaneously but gradually.

SUMMARY

Manufacturing caricatures
Manufacturing needs to shed its traditional image and proactively manage its leap into the future. This involves:
- breaking down the barriers to communication and co-operation

within the factory and with external partners
- treating suppliers as partners in achieving missions
- recognising the importance of the environment
- taking time and resources to experiment with new processes
- empowering employees by pushing responsibility down through the hierarchy
- developing closer co-operation between product development and production
- removing barriers between the factory and the customer.

7 THE GLOBALISATION CHALLENGE

The globalisation challenge raises specific issues for the manufacturing function. The integrated factory works within a network of partners encompassing all of a company's factories. Spread across countries, such networks need international coordination. What does it mean to manufacture globally, and what are some of the challenges created by the emergence of the single European market are the questions addressed by this chapter.

THINKING IN NETWORKS

Having several plants does not necessarily imply international manufacturing. Networks of plants can be limited to a single country. But the need for companies to possess an international dimension grows steadily stronger. New conditions, ranging from market specifications, global standards, and trade legislation, to global competitors and improved production methods are all forcing companies to leave their home ground.

Companies manufacturing on an international scale cannot limit their thinking to any single plant. Manufacturing resources must be seen as networks of factories. Kasra Ferdows[1] has developed a fairly simple model that offers an initial idea of the relationships between networked factories. Based on a study of electronic products manufacturers, he concluded that factories could be analysed based on two main criteria.

---

[1] Ferdows, K., 1989, *International Manufacturing*, North Holland, New York.

The strategy behind the factory

The first dimension describes the primary strategic reason for a factory's existence. Why was it created? The second dimension is the type of activities carried out at a given site.

Three major reasons for establishing a factory were established:

- access to markets
- access to technology
- access to low cost production factors.

Access to markets

Market access can take different forms. Food companies such as Nestlé or Unilever like to set up factories close to their biggest or most sophisticated markets to be in a position to pick up market signals quickly. Following the same logic, producers of soya sauce may benefit from a location in Southeast Asia, while cheese producers may want to keep an eye on France.

Companies also set up factories to overcome barriers restricting imports of products not produced locally. Nissan and Toyota created assembly lines in the UK to avoid stringent EC restrictions on sales of Japanese cars in Europe. Digital Equipment Corporation's decision to open a plant in Brazil seemed a dubious investment from a purely economic standpoint. But it was the only way for DEC to access a major Latin American market.

This motivation is also behind the location of factories producing very large sized products. Rockwool is a very light, relatively cheap but very bulky insulation material. Production must be relatively close to the company's end users otherwise transport costs are too high. The same is true for very weighty low value products, such as bricks.

Access to technological resources

Access to technological resources is a second motivation in choosing plant locations. While large Japanese automobile assembly lines requiring a lot of relatively cheap labour go to the

UK or Spain, specialised high-tech automotive suppliers prefer the Mulhouse-Stuttgart-München triangle, where some of Europe's finest car producers and suppliers are based. Such choices guarantee a local network reflecting each company's requirements in terms of trained labour and technicians, and access to formal and informal information exchange.

This last point is crucial. Stephan Schräder[2] described patterns in the exchange of expertise and information in the US mini-mill industry. He found out that such trading has nothing in common with leaks, industrial espionage or friendly gossip. Instead, he explains it by the rational behaviour of the employees studied, who give information in order to obtain information from their competitors. The study also demonstrates that there is a clear relation between a firm's inclination to participate in informal know-how trading and its economic performance.

One could expect stable, traditional networks between technical employees and managers of competing firms in a particular region. But one would assume that the entrance of new competitors, foreign or domestic, would reduce the intensity of information exchange within the network. Yet, on the contrary, the inclination to cooperate and to participate in informal know-how trading increases considerably with these new (and often foreign) competitors.

This can be explained by the riskiness of information trading. The pay-offs of cooperation are uncertain, and offering and receiving information does not occur concurrently. Under such conditions, managers and technical employees could be expected to develop a rather conservative attitude, limiting information trading with newcomers. But it appears that the arrival of new competitors from outside the traditional boundaries of an industry actually increases both the benefits of trading and the costs of being uncooperative.

Foreign competition forces existing firms to innovate constantly in order to remain competitive. Under such pressure, firms cannot remain unco-operative. They must use their own know-how as

[2] Stephan Schräder, 1991, 'Informal Technology Transfer Between Firms: Cooperation Through Information Trading', *Research Policy*, Vol. 20, no. 2, pp. 153–170.

cards to barter for the know-how of newcomers. A factory which has been created to tap into local technological resources must be quickly absorbed into the local network so that it can channel the information it obtains to headquarters or to other plants in the group.

Access to low cost production factors

The location of factories can also be decided based on the cost of imports or labour. Oil refineries and petrochemical plants locate near oil wells or in large ports where supplying raw materials is relatively easy. Low labour costs are behind the many textile factories sprouting up in Pakistan, Sri Lanka or Mauritius, and of electronic assembly plants in Southeast Asia. There is also a steep increase in the creation of software development groups in India and the Philippines, both countries with low cost information workers.

Tax benefits provided by governments are another potential low cost production factor. They can make capital investments less expensive, but careful evaluation is required. This type of advantage often proves ephemeral, and may seduce top management into taking decisions which are not wholly rational. Generally, the location of factories should first be determined by management considerations. Tax breaks and other government incentives should be taken into account in subsequent iterations of the decision-making process.

The second dimension: how much value added?

The second dimension proposed in Ferdows' framework is the nature and degree of technical work carried out on the site. Are activities limited to final assembly and testing, or is there some simple component production? Does the plant develop its own procedures for quality and maintenance? Does it have its own process engineering, or a fully-fledged development department? This dimension is the expression of a site's degree of technical value-added. It is linked to the talents and scope of the workforce, the quality of management and the level of capital investment.

COMBINING THE TWO DIMENSIONS

The two dimensions help us analyse networks of factories. Figure 7.1 illustrates the mapping of some typical factories. They are simple examples. Factories can be found anywhere across the map, and in some cases they may occupy two or more positions.

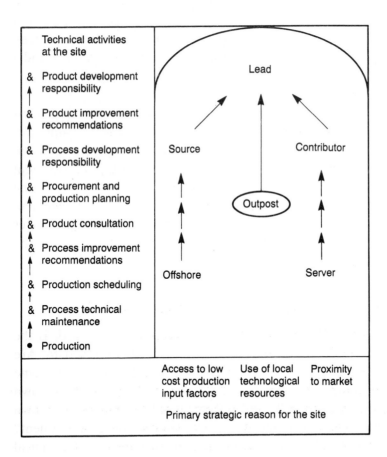

Figure 7.1 Changes in strategic roles of international factories (Ferdows 1989)

Offshore plants

A typical offshore production plant has limited technical activities and seeks to maximise access to low cost production factors. Such plants are found in many export free processing zones in Southeast Asia, in the Maquiladores zones of Mexico, or among the recently created assembly lines of Eastern Europe.

Source plants

When these plants develop more technical activities they become source plants, that is, they become sources, for the rest of the world, of particular products or management methods. Such an evolution is illustrated by Hewlett Packard's Singapore factory. HP created it years ago as an offshore facility for assembling calculators and other simple electronic products. Building on its creativity and its increasing level of technical activities, the plant became a source of quality management methods. It developed its own processes and received global product development responsibility for a range of the company's products. Today, it fulfils the role of a source plant. It should be noted that, today, Singapore's government has an active policy of upgrading offshore plants to source factory status.

Server plants

Some plants choose their locations for market reasons, and operate with limited technical activities. In these cases, the plant's main task is serving the market. Food processing factories are one example. Assembly lines of completely knocked-down (CKD) car kits found in Indonesia, Thailand or Latin America are another.

Contributor plants

When server plants expand their technical activities, they call on local suppliers of components and services. In the process, they make a real contribution to the development of the local industrial network. Many of the US multinationals which set up factories in

Europe in the 1950s and early 1960s, following the Marshall plan, subsequently became key contributors. The petrochemical plants surrounding the Belgian port of Antwerp were created to serve the European market. Over the years, their interaction with local suppliers, neighbouring schools and universities and socio-political representatives created a dense network supporting the city's push to become the world's second largest petrochemical complex after Houston.

Technological outposts

Factories created to access technology, which remain with a limited range of activities can be called technological outposts. Their main function is to create a window on technology. But to be an effective outpost, they need to develop their own activities enough to be taken seriously by others in the local network. They need to possess enough worthwhile data to be allowed to participate in the information exchange. In the biotechnology field, many offshoots of large companies set themselves up in California so that they can benefit from the local network of excellent specialised researchers.

European companies have often failed to recognise the importance of being actively involved in production as a step to being accepted into Japan's industrial network. Several European companies created technological antennae in Japan, but failed to benefit from them because they contented themselves with being receivers of information, and had nothing to contribute.

Partner or lead plants

Some outposts develop a full range of technological activities. They become real partners in the local industrial network. They give and receive technology, developing it locally for use around the world. They use local technicians and scientists, they stimulate local suppliers and create partnerships with universities and research institutes. Sometimes the company's foreign origins begin to fade or be forgotten. IBM's policy is to behave as a local company in the different countries in which it operates. In Japan, for example, in addition to factories, it has its own research and development labs. Before Fujitsu became the leading mainframe manufacturer, IBM had long been recognised as Japan's leading mainframe manufacturer.

MANAGING THE NETWORK

Categorising factories is fine, but is it more than an academic exercise? The purpose of these classifications is to help readers analyse their own factories or the location of their operations in the context of their business strategies and networks.

Based on observations of excellent international performers, three points should be kept in mind.

Factory charters

First, make sure that you have factories in different areas of the map. It makes little sense to manage a collection of clones copied from the company's original factory. Factories have their own history and development, and they may be partners or contributors. Serving new markets on the other side of the world may not require another partner, but rather a server or a source factory. Each factory needs to define a clear charter along both of the map's dimensions: why is the factory needed? What is the technical added value that it creates? A company's portfolio of factories should reflect a diversified set of charters.

Performance measurement

Make sure that the control mechanisms used to track factory performance are adapted to the charter. This may sound obvious, but all too often companies use a uniform system for performance measurement. Factories often have trouble meeting performance targets based on the experiences of factories with different charters. This can lead to ineffective or even dysfunctional factory management behaviour.

An American manufacturer of industrial control systems demonstrates how performance control systems can run amok. A product was launched in 1975 with a very good manufacturing strategy. It was based on a system of centralised components factories in the US which interacted with a series of decentralised factories close to the company's major markets which did the assembly. The product's phenomenal success quickly caused capacity shortages in the central components factories. The decentralised European factory suggested building its own components facility.

The new factory was to be a server factory. Its charter was quite clear: the European factory would be dedicated to the local market, would have no engineering, and would limit itself to production and assembly. Like any typical US based multinational in the 1970s, headquarters set the European plant the same control systems and performance targets it had in its American factories, whose production volume was three times as great. The European factory was quickly regarded as being in trouble because it was not being measured for market responsiveness (the charter of a server plant) but on efficiency (the charter of a source or offshore plant).

The consequences were painfully predictable. The European component factory's manager inflated demand and squeezed suppliers for better prices, harming delivery lead times in the process; the plant became extremely unresponsive. It demanded long-term forecasts, so as to reduce switch-over time and cost. As long as the market was expanding, this behaviour did not cause too much damage. But as soon as the market stabilised, inventories popped up all over the logistics chain. Was the factory manager at fault? He had created the problems by sub-optimising the factory. But it was actually the control system that was responsible through its inability to recognise the difference in factory charters.

Control systems must be adapted to charters. A partner plant has to be measured on the basis of its technical contribution and on the speed with which it can diffuse its innovations throughout the company. Server plants should be measured for market responsiveness, and the extent to which they are able to understand and respond to customer needs. Offshore plants should be measured on cost, and cost alone.

Network dynamics

The bottom line of managing manufacturing networks is managing the network's dynamics. Charters change over time, and if left to factory managers, plants will tend to move towards the top of the diagram, in the interests of personal self preservation. The higher the positioning, the more technical value is added at the site, the more assets there are, and the more difficult it becomes to close the plants.

Local plant managers, who have a stake in the growth and the survival of their plant, will try to develop it by extending the range of technical activities carried out at the site. It is also simply a more motivating job. But this may not be what the company is after. If plants are all contributors, servers or partners, the flexibility to reallocate capacities across different sectors is lost. This loss reduces the company's ability to exploit the major advantage of manufacturing on an international scale: flexible responses to shifts and cycles in international markets, technologies, and cost structures.

Evolutions in position on the map should be carefully managed and controlled. That does not necessarily imply that the charter be defined top down in a dictatorial fashion. But it should centrally set boundaries in the map within which plant managers can adjust their factories' charters.

IMPLEMENTING THE INTERNATIONAL NETWORK

In the development and growth of international plant networks several areas are critical, but three are key: the need for improving communications, the management of a global logistics network and the organisational focus to be used.

Communicating internationally

Communication is essential to any management activity and any breakdown in communication guarantees trouble. Across time zones, linguistic differences and cultural specificities, organisational partners become increasingly difficult to manage. Manufacturing internationally requires that special care be paid to connections ensuring coordination and integrity across factories.

Sociometric studies several decades old proved that the probability of fault-free communication between two individuals decreases rapidly in direct relation to the distance that separates them. Distance cannot be completely compensated for by modern communication techniques such as fax, telephone, videoconferencing or computer networks. Face to face communication remains essential.

The author has studied the impact of sophisticated electronic communications on behaviour in technical organisations.[3] Though the organisations studied were more development and engineering oriented, one could generalise the findings to any technical environment, including manufacturing. Findings show that in order to collaborate across borders, team members need to reach a certain threshold of mutual trust. This threshold is very difficult to reach if there is no face-to-face contact at all. Once the members of the team have met they can return to their respective locations. Due to imperfect communication, misunderstandings are likely to arise resulting in a gradual erosion of trust. This then plunges below the minimum level required for effective communication.

Sophisticated electronic communication systems such as video or computer conferencing created the hope that this decline could be stopped. But even the most sophisticated systems do not entirely eliminate the fall. The 'half-life time', the time it takes to have the trust drop below the minimum threshold, may be lengthened, but not indefinitely. Even exceedingly well organised systems have their limits. An example is a company that designed a video conferencing room with an oval table which was cut in half,

---

[3] De Meyer, A., 1991, Tech Talk, 'How Managers are Stimulating Global R & D Communication', *Sloan Management Review*, Spring 1991, pp. 49–58.

and where the other half of the table was a projection screen filled with another group of people who were thousands of kilometres away. Even in such a realistically simulated environment, distrust eventually crept back into the conversation.

Consequently, companies must carefully manage the evolution of levels of trust, have systems to reduce its decline, and regularly organise face-to-face meetings to give lagging trust a needed boost.

The global logistics network

All the problems a company may face in its local supply and distribution network also exist when working on an international scale – only more so. Logistical issues such as supplier reliability, distribution delays or inventory management are all compounded by distance. National differences in distribution practices and transport infrastructures, administrative difficulties with border crossings and diversity of language or culture further complicate things.

There is a trade-off worth considering in this context. Global procurement ensures the most advantageous cost, quality and delivery reliability. But long distance procurements often include communication problems with suppliers. These can be particularly devastating if suppliers are also co-designers or co-developers.

As Clark and Fujimoto[4] have shown in the automobile industry, the role of suppliers in the development of sub-assemblies and components can be very important. Japanese automobile producers have more than 60 per cent of their components developed by their suppliers on an exclusive basis. Having suppliers develop components contributes to the speed of development and increases development efficiency. But it works well only if there is intensive communication between the main contractor and suppliers. Clearly, keeping suppliers a short distance from factories guarantees short communication lines. But this impedes the creation of a worldwide network of suppliers based on suppliers

---

[4] Clark, K. and Fujimoto, T., 1991, *Product Development Performance, Strategy, Organisation and Management in the World Auto Industry*, Harvard Business School Press, Boston.

with the most competitive cost, wherever the supplier is based.

Long distance Just-in-Time supplier relations can also prove difficult. They are not impossible, but they demand very creative approaches. Sony and Tektronic had a Just-in-Time delivery process between Japan and the West Coast of the US. The supply chain was as short as the flight from Tokyo to Seattle. Other solutions are possible. Rank Xerox's joint venture in Europe received more than 50 per cent of its copier supplies from outside Europe. In order to ensure Just-in-Time delivery to the factory, they created a concentrator warehouse a few kilometres from the factory, situated in Northern France and they subcontracted the task of managing it. For this arrangement to succeed, intense cooperation between Rank Xerox and the subcontractor was imperative. Why was the decision made? Not to offload the factory's inventory on a subcontractor, creating another filter in the delivery system. On the contrary, the company wanted to smooth worldwide Just-in-Time delivery by getting a specialist to manage it.

Product or process oriented?

Internationalising logistics requires a clear choice about the guiding principles of a factory network. For example, is it product or process oriented? Product oriented factories produce finished products or sub-assemblies for the region in which they are located. Process oriented factories specialise in a particular process and treatment and apply it to any, or all, of a company's products.

Product oriented factories have the advantage of reducing transportation and logistics costs, but they may be too small to be economical. Process oriented factories reach economies of scale in their processes, but can lead to a lot of shuffling around of components between factories. In a world of high transportation costs and significant barriers between countries, product oriented factories seem to be favoured. If the world economy becomes freer and if companies improve the management of their logistics network, a trend could develop towards process oriented factories.

International production organisation

Local organisational structures, whether they are functional or matrix, are often not adapted to international operations. Matrix organisations may exist on paper, but the intensity of communication needed to make them work is often impossible to attain internationally. In functional organisations, reporting over thousands of kilometres and in a foreign language has many potential pitfalls. There are no miracle solutions for the ultimate international manufacturing organisation, except that it should be adapted to the products it is producing and the nature of the network in which it is operating. Two suggestions can, however, be helpful.

First, whatever the structure, factory managers should have a geographical and functional matrix in their minds, as Bartlett and Ghoshal have suggested.[5] For decision making, it is important for manufacturing managers to have the reflex to integrate the impact of their decisions on other factories and functions, worldwide.

Secondly, one of the most important challenges on an international scale is the company's ability to transfer and disseminate what one factory learns to other factories. The speed of this transferring will determine international manufacturing performance. Any factory, whether it is offshore, partner or contributor, will develop some know-how relevant to the rest of the organisation. Nobody in a factory network has a monopoly on knowledge. Channels for the diffusion of the learning need to be established, requiring that companies realise that every factory must become a centre of excellence in its own right.

THE IMPACT OF EUROPEAN UNIFICATION

The results of what is commonly called 'Europe 1992' and the promises of the Maastricht treaty have had and will continue to have a profound impact on international manufacturing. What was

---

[5] Bartlett, C.A. and Ghoshal, S., 1989, *Managing Across Borders*, Harvard Business School Press, Boston.

a collection of countries with distinct logistical infrastructures and market characteristics is moving towards a heterogeneous but relatively open market. That implies that companies will have to review – if not revise – the charters of their European plants, as well as the logistical and organisational structures of their manufacturing functions.

An example is Honeywell. This US based producer of control systems had 16 subsidiaries, 13 factories and about 10,500 employees in Europe. They also had a distribution centre, 700 distributors, and more than 2,000 suppliers. In preparation for the single market, Honeywell began a major revision of its logistics network in 1990. The goal was to remove internal barriers and improve the flow of goods and information within the organisation.

In the past, each partner tended to develop its own, nationally oriented, logic. In principle, any movement of components or products was supposed to pass through the distribution centre in Amsterdam. But products 'escaped' this obligatory passage. Factories created parallel flows amongst themselves. This led to uncontrollable buffer stocks everywhere in the company.

The solution was radically European. The goals for 1995 include direct flow from factories to distributors, a unified European database system accessible to all partners in the logistics chain, including customers. Such a European approach should provide operating economies of FF 31 million, and savings of FF 280 million for inventory reductions. The scale of the distribution centre in Amsterdam has to be redefined, stocks of finished products in subsidiaries have to be drastically reduced and will be managed on a pan-European level, and production will be made to order rather than to stock. What is happening in Europe now offers Honeywell a model for its global manufacturing tomorrow.

My own research in the European Manufacturing Futures project shows that in preparing for the unified market, European companies are tending to reduce the number of their suppliers and to keep the number of factories stable. But they are shifting them from a product orientation to a process orientation, serving more markets than before. Moreover, they expect more demand for automation, and plan to respond with process oriented factories making entire ranges of sub-assemblies, which feed into small local factories for final assembly and testing. In order to succeed in this, they are increasingly adopting the concept of delayed differentiation, described in Chapter 5.

SUMMARY

Developing networks of factories
Define the strategy behind each factory. Was it established to gain access to:
- markets
- technology
- or low cost production factors.

Establish how much value added is carried out at the site, ranging from final assembly and testing to full-fledged development department.
   Combining the two dimensions above leads to classifiying each site as one of the following types of plants:
- offshore
- source
- server
- technological outpost
- contributor
- partner.

Managing the network
- establish clear charters for each factory
- development performance measurements based on the charters
- take into account the dynamic of networks over time.

Implementing international networks
- communication increases in importance as companies extend their geographic breadth
- global logistics are far more complicated than local applications.

Trade offs between global procurement or JIT policies must be weighed.

- a key decision is whether the network will be process or product oriented
- matrix organisation reasoning is essential for managers in the international network.

8 IMPLEMENTATION (I) – CREATING LASTING IMPROVEMENTS

Previous chapters have addressed the definition of a manufacturing strategy. Fixing objectives is one thing, implementing them quite another. The next two chapters study two aspects of this issue: creating improvements with staying power; and introducing change more quickly.

TRADITIONAL IMPLEMENTATION

The traditional model of manufacturing strategy suggests that manufacturing decisions must correspond to manufacturing missions. This was briefly referred to in Chapter 3 and is explained further in Figure 8.1. Hayes and Wheelwright[1] propose that, in manufacturing, ten categories of decisions need to be taken. They divide them into two groups: the structural and the infrastructural.

Structural decisions involve investments in brick and mortar and major technological investments: Where to build plants? What kind of process technology to use? How large should the factory be, i.e. what will be its aggregate production capacity? And what will be made and what will be bought from suppliers? These decisions commit the factory in the long-term and are not easy to change, once the investment has been made. Opening and closing a factory, replacing all the process technology, or changing the output capacity of a factory are not decisions to be taken or modified easily.

Infrastructural decisions concern systems and procedures: what kind of quality management system will be implemented? How are

---

[1] Hayes, R.M. and Wheelwright, S.G., 1984, *Restoring a Competitive Edge*, Wiley and Sons.

human resources managed? What kind of organisational structure will be created? How is the flow of goods and information managed, resulting in what kind of production planning and inventory control system? How do you control organisational performance? What kind of system do you need to support the development and introduction of new products and processes?

Unlike structural decisions, some gradual shifts in infrastructural categories are feasible. That does not mean that they are less important or that they require less commitment, they are simply less of a one-off decision. Policies in human resource management, for example, can be adapted over time, or quality management systems can be adapted step by step.

In each category, decisions need to be made by manufacturing managers. And they have choices. They can opt for either a manual or a highly automated approach to production. They can choose flat organisational structures with networked, autonomous teams or traditional hierarchies. They can establish factories in Ireland, Switzerland or Singapore. None of these choices is intrinsically good or bad. They must simply correspond to corporate strategy, or even help build and reinforce it.

If a company wants to compete on flexibility and customisation in the market place, it must invest in two things: flexible manufacturing systems, spread out over several smaller factories; and employee development to ensure that its workforce can cope with a wide range of diverse tasks. If, however, price and cost efficiency are the objective, a company needs to invest in efficient automation (probably concentrated in one large unit) to achieve high economies of scale. It will also have to choose suppliers on a cost performance basis.

There is no perfect portfolio of choices in these decision categories because there is no single perfect production system. But for every strategy, there is an optional and coherent choice to be made in each of the ten categories.

Building the link between business strategy and decision categories is not straightforward. A well-defined portfolio of order-winning and qualifying missions in manufacturing is a prerequisite. As suggested in Figure 8.1, a portfolio of missions is the crucial communication between the worlds of business strategy and manufacturing.

Implementing a manufacturing strategy is typically a two step process. First, the business strategy must be clearly translated into a portfolio of qualifying and order-winning manufacturing missions. Secondly, a coherent set of choices must be taken in each of the decision categories, corresponding to the portfolio of missions, as explained in Chapter 3.

When Toshiba took over a colour television plant in the UK in the beginning of the 80s, it set itself the objective of delivering on time – all the time, keeping costs under strict control by reducing inventories, scrap and rework and improving manufacturing lead times. The core mission of the plant was the delivery reliability, combined with cost efficiency.

Televisions happen to be a seasonal product. Orders are much higher in the second semester of the year. Toshiba could have ensured delivery reliability by building up inventories during the first half of the year, but that would have conflicted with its cost efficiency objective. To fulfil its porfolio of missions, the plant established a seasonal working system. Permanent staff work 37.5 hours per week in the low season (January to July) and 42.5 hours

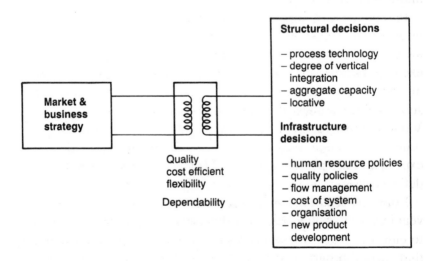

Figure 8.1 Traditional model of manufacturing strategy

during the peak period in the second half of the year. At the same time, staff training programmes were developed to reach maximum flexibility. Flexibility enhancing reward systems and salary scales complemented the effort of adapting human resource policies to the portfolio of missions. Even policies on new product introduction were adapted to the delivery reliability mission. New products which usually lead to a reduction in output, are now introduced during the winter, when demand is low, because there is slack capacity in the factory. This illustrates how several manufacturing decisions can be adapted to support the portfolio of missions.

Personal experience with the model

Over the past decade, I have had the opportunity of seeing this model in use in many of the more than 100 factories that I have visited, quite a lot of them twice or more. In many, choices were made and decisions taken following the traditional model of manufacturing strategy. In some cases this was a conscious approach, in others unconscious. Over time, I began to observe that the implementation of this model led to two types of improvements in manufacturing performance.

In some cases, improvements proved durable. In others, improvements had been obtained, but, after a while, disappeared again. At every factory visit, factory management had a new exciting manufacturing programme to show: a particular quality management programme with a catchy title ('Quality is our First Job', 'Value Creation through Total Quality Control', 'Quality has Value'); a programme to implement autonomous work groups in order to broaden jobs and increase employee motivation; an experiment with flexible automation or another with a just-in-time delivery system.

I often visited the same factory several times, at three or four year intervals. And it was only over time that the differences began to emerge. When management was asked what had happened to that terrific programme of yesteryear, there were two types of answers. Either my hosts explained that the programme had been

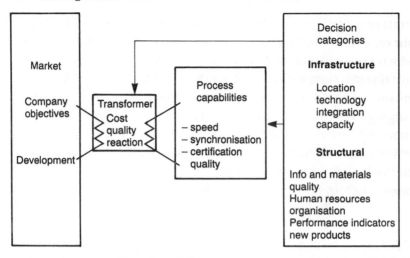

Source: De Meyer and Van Wassenhove, 1992

Figure 8.2   Creating manufacturing capabilities

successful, the required results obtained, and the company was now focusing on other priorities. They seemed almost embarrassed when I referred back to a programme introduced a few years earlier. Yet I could see that the positive results had withered away, and that some of the old bad habits had resurfaced. Or they enthusiastically described the results of the older programme, and proudly showed that it was the basis for new improvement programmes. These programmes had had a *lasting* impact on the performance of the factory.

So what does it take to create lasting performance improvements? What is the difference between performance improvements which fade furtively away and those which stay and nourish continued improvements? It became clear to my colleagues and me,[2] that companies must not only make their choices in each decision category based on corporate strategy, but that they must also develop the capabilities to implement them (Figure 8.2).

The difference with the traditional view of manufacturing

---

[2] The ideas in the rest of this chapter build upon the work by Kasra Ferdows and myself, described in Ferdows, K. and De Meyer, A., 1990, Lasting improvements in Manufacturing Management, Journal of Operations Management, Vol. 9, no. 2, pp. 168–184

strategy is that quality, reliability, cost efficiency and flexibility are not only possible missions. They also describe sets of capabilities which can be developed and which can then be used in creating sustainable competitive advantage. Quality can simply be a mission. But its relentless pursuit helps companies gain wide ranging expertise and intellectual assets for creating quality. A company that is truly committed to quality can also earn, in the process, a workforce with automatic reflexes for constantly improving product and process quality. But how are these hidden capabilities, or lasting improvements created?

CREATING LASTING PERFORMANCE IMPROVEMENTS

In explaining the concept of creating lasting improvements in manufacturing, K. Ferdows and I developed the analogy of a sand cone (Figure 8.3), with the sand representing the resources and management efforts invested in improving manufacturing. There are two basic assumptions in this model:

- that a particular sequence exists in the creation of capabilities
- that capabilities are cumulative, and build upon each other.

When starting with an unsatisfactory manufacturing situation, the first thing to invest in is quality. The first grains of 'sand' will be used to increase the organisation's ability to produce high quality output, and get its processes under control. Only when the sand cone has grown sufficiently high (when quality has reached satis-factory levels) can investment in the second layer start: production dependability and delivery reliability.

But to invest in dependability – and thereby increase the height of the cone – one must simultaneously broaden its base. For the cone to be stable, adding sand at the top of the cone requires adding sand at the bottom. That is what is meant by the cumulative nature of creating capabilities: dependability cannot be improved without increasing quality capabilities.

Once the company has reached a high enough level of

dependability and a broad enough basis in quality, it can start investing in the third level of capabilities: reaction speed. But again the same mechanism plays. In order to improve the company's reaction speed to changing customer demands and specifications, it has to broaden its basis in both quality and dependability.

Only when capabilities in quality, dependability and reaction speed are strong enough, can the company invest in the final phase: cost reduction. This is extremely important. Lasting cost improvements are the *consequence*, not the launching pad, of other improvements and capability creation in manufacturing. Cost improvements that remain after artificial pressures to impose them disappear are the consequence of many other actions.

This does not mean that a badly managed factory's major cost reduction programme would have no effect, even if it does not improve quality, dependability and reaction speed. The model's implicit assumption is that the factory is more or less well managed and that there are no obvious cost cutting exercises to be done. In other words, the factory works at what economists call its 'economic frontier'. This means that it is as efficient as it can be given its current level of resource constraints. If this fairly efficient factory wants to improve its cost efficiency, it must start in other areas. Cost improvements are the result of other improvements.

That broadening the quality base leads to cost reduction is now well accepted. But improvements in reaction speed also lead to significant cost reductions. Since 1988 Aérospatiale, the French aerospace company, has invested in a system of just-in-time deliveries in order to reduce work in process and manufacturing lead times for the production of Airbus and ATR planes. It has been able to reduce manufacturing lead times for component elements of the cockpit of the ATR or the A340 from 18 to five weeks in two years. It took a reorganisation of production lines and investments of less than 2 million French Francs. This also translated into an overall reduction of work in process by as much as 20 per cent in the assembly line. Costs were reduced by more than 200 million French Francs.

The recovery of the French automobile producer Renault is a

clear example of the sand cone model. In the middle of the 1980s, the company was virtually bankrupt. Renault started a major rationalisation of its factories around 1985, by first bringing its factories closer to their economic frontier. Drastic cost reductions were implemented, employment levels were greatly decreased, and factories were closed. Once the factories had become more or less efficient, given their existing resources, Renault started a major quality improvement programme. This was soon followed by improvements in reliability in sticking to customer promises. The results of the total quality programme have been very visible in Renault's dramatic defect reductions. For the past few years, the company has started to invest in flexibility, and has found that the cost improvements which were obtained with sweat and tears in the middle of the 1980s, now come almost automatically as the result of efforts in quality management and reaction speed.

In summary, the sand cone model approach suggests that in order to create lasting improvements in manufacturing, the following steps need to be followed:

- while implementing a set of choices with respect to the ten decision categories described in line with the portfolio of missions, create a set of core manufacturing capabilities or competencies
- to create a stable set of capabilities, a certain sequence must be respected:
    1. quality capabilities
    2. capabilities in dependable production and delivery, and reaction speed
    3. cost reduction capabilities
- these capabilities are cumulative and support each other. As a consequence, additional investments in any one requires a simultaneous broadening of the capability set that precedes it in the sequence
- for companies operating at the economic frontier, lasting cost improvements are the result of, not the prerequisite for, improvements in other areas.

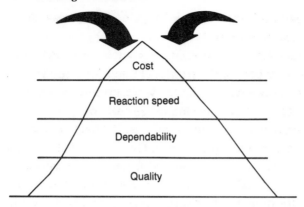

Figure 8.3 The sandcone model of lasting improvements in manufacturing

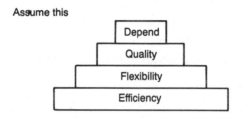

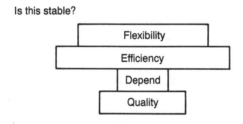

Figure 8.4 What if we have the wrong sequence?

Not respecting the sequence

If we assume that the sand cone represents a sound approach to improving manufacturing performance, what happens if the proposed sequence is not respected? Assume that manufacturing improvements are implemented according to a caricatured 'Taylorian' approach: costs are cut and with the margins created, investments are made in improving delivery dependability, product quality and reaction speed.

What kind of a sand cone is produced? Figure 8.4 shows how unstable the sand cone becomes. With some support and lots of glue, it may teeter temporarily in the unstable situation shown at the bottom of the figure. But this cannot last forever – although some manufacturing plants try. The support and the glue are more commonly called 'crisis managers'. Because the plant is under competitive pressure, the crisis manager is brought in to slash costs quickly. This is usually quite successful. After all, if the crisis is big enough and motivation high enough, it is not difficult to dramatically cut costs in a six month interval.

But what happens then? The successful crisis manager moves on. And as the plant door closes behind him, old habits return apace. The artificial sand construction proves to be nothing more than fiction. Costs rise and often the factory's old quality, dependability or reaction speed capabilities have been destroyed by cost cutting. Of course, I am not implying that in a badly managed plant, operating far from its economic frontier, cost cutting programmes would not have both positive and lasting results. But in a normal, adequately run plant, cost improvements based on short-term action, without simultaneous investment in other capabilities, will not survive after the crisis manager's tenure.

An illustration: the Philips Washington plant

The 1990 competition for Britain's best factories[3] described Philips Components' factory in Washington, Tyne and Wear. The plant produced deflection units for TV sets. It was probably an archetypal victim of Far Eastern competition: remote from decision-making and fierce cost pressures, it was responsible for neither design nor sales. Yet the plant had conducted some major strides towards the end of the 1980s. Rather than simply implementing a series of improvements, plant management had under-

---

[3] See Coulkin, S., 1990, 'Britain's best factories', *Management Today*, November, pp. 66–74.

stood that it had to create and build capabilities on the basis of its existing assets.

The improvement was based on sophisticated engineering which attempted to leverage employee skills, rather than supplant them. Just as important as the technology and the engineering, was the factory's new organisation. It had evolved into a series of focused factories, managed as individual businesses and run by an integrated, multifunctional team, led by a facilitator.

These changes were facilitated by new pay structures, a flatter organisation, and a vast two-way communication effort which discussed and explained the changes at all levels. Laudable as the improvements are, everyone was convinced that they are only markers along the way to continuous improvements and the creation of fundamental production capabilities.

The first objective had been to improve internal quality. First time yields increased from 72 per cent to 98 per cent. That was good, but not enough to stay in business. The second goal was creating an integrated process, including components suppliers, that would enable 100 per cent delivery performance. By the end of 1989, the plant had attained a 97 per cent delivery performance. Yet again, this was not enough.

Plant management considered that quality and customer satisfaction were concepts of the 1980s. To win in the 1990s, they were convinced that they had to go beyond customer expectations. That required not only unquestionable product quality and reliability, but also a lot of influence over design and engineering in order to improve the launch of new products by speeding up reaction times.

The pattern described in this chapter appears clearly. After an initial clean up of the manufacturing organisation, the plant tackled quality issues. After that, it dealt with issues of dependability, and afterwards turned its attention to reaction speed. But the last move was only feasible if the company continued its relentless pursuit of manufacturing quality and dependability.

SUMMARY

Implementing manufacturing decisions

In implementation, ten categories of decisions need to be taken, following the Hayes and Wheelwright model, divided into two groups.

Structural
- plant location
- type of process technology
- aggregate production capacity
- what will be made and what will be bought from subcontractors.

Infrastructural
- type of quality management system
- style of human resource management
- type of organisational structure
- flow of goods and information management
- type of planning and inventory control systems
- new product development policy.

Creating lasting improvements

The sequence in implementing improvements is important:
1. quality capabilities first
2. reliable production and delivery, reaction speed
3. cost reduction capabilities

Capabilities provide cumulative support for each other. Any improvement in one must be matched by equivalent shifts in the categories that precede it in the sequence.

9 IMPLEMENTATION (II) – THE KEY TO DIFFERENTIATION

This chapter studies in greater detail the decision categories evoked in the previous chapter. Over the last decade we have seen a series of comprehensive programmes such as Statistical Quality Control, Total Quality Control, Six Sigma programmes, Just-in-Time, Time-based Competition, Creating Value for the Customer, etc. The frustrating fact for many senior manufacturing managers is that these programmes always seem to originate with the competition, forcing their own companies to scramble to catch up.

Is there a way of predicting what the next miracle programme will be? The question itself is rooted in a misconception. There simply is no such thing as the one truly miraculous programme – there are many. The real challenge is identifying the one that fits corporate requirements and organising the company to implement it faster than the competition.

THE FACTORY OF THE FUTURE

What should the factory of the future look like, and what kind of programmes need to be implemented to make today's factories evolve? Is the integrated factory described in chapter 6 the solution? An answer may lie in an analysis of the results of the Global Manufacturing Survey.[1] Table 9.1 presents an overview of the five

---

[1] Miller, J.G., De Meyer, A. and Nakane, J., 1992, *Benchmarking Global Manufacturing*, Business One Irwin, Homewood, Illinois.

most significant pay-offs (out of a list of 26) resulting from past improvement programmes as well as the five most important programmes for the future.

The first set of programmes reveals remarkable differences in planned manufacturing improvement investments in the US, Europe and Japan. In the US, programmes focus strongly on employees and teams of employees. North American manufacturers have eagerly accepted the argument that the greatest advances in quality and cost will come from increasing workforce contributions and by breaking down functional boundaries. By pushing responsibility down through the organisational pyramid and overcoming bureaucracy with cross-functional teams, Americans want to improve their ability to create the value factory of the future and lower its cost.

In contrast, Japanese manufacturers put their emphasis on the development and improvement of fundamental process technologies. Along with information systems integration, this strong orientation towards process development supports a push towards factories capable of making reliable, rapid design changes to customised products. The Japanese design factory of the future will be founded on new processes that overcome the enormous complexity involved in delivering large numbers of new, customised, high quality products with short lead times.

European manufacturers are investing in a variety of programmes and activities. This suggests that their organisations are restructuring to adapt to the nascent pan-European market, with shifts in culture, coordination techniques, and organisational structures. Europe's investment in integrated information systems, for example, aims to enhance the coordination of activities across borders. Quality function deployment pushes firms to design products that satisfy new European markets. Training develops new skills and competitive new cultures based on a vision of borderless factories.

Whether based on a vision of a value factory, a design factory, or a borderless factory, each region's factories are focused on the development of organisations whose manufacturing and strategy are tightly interwoven.

United States	Europe	Japan
1. Linking manufacturing strategy to business strategy	Linking manufacturing strategy to business strategy	Integration of information systems in manufacturing and across factories
2. Giving workers broader tasks and more responsibilities	Integrating information systems in manufacturing	Developing new processes for new products
3. Statistical process control	Quality function deployment	Production and inventory control systems
4. Worker and supervisor training	Training of supervisors, workers and managers	Developing new processes for existing products
5. Creation of interfunctional work teams	Integrating information systems across factories	Linking manufacturing strategy to business strategy

Source: J. G. Miller et al, 1992

Table 9.1a Most important future improvement programme

United States	Europe	Japan
1. Interfunctional work teams	Training of supervisors	Developing new processes for existing products
2. Manufacturing reorganisation	Manufacturing reorganisation	Developing new processes for new products
3. Statistical process control	Linking manufacturing strategy to business strategy	Quality circles
4. Linking manufacturing to business strategy	Quality function deployment	Computer-aided design
5.	Developing new processes for new products	Quality function deployment

Source: J. G. Miller et al, 1992

Table 9.1b Pay-off of past improvement programme

Though manufacturers in the three regions have evolved towards similar positions, the approaches they took in getting there were quite diverse. Both the similarities and differences are intriguing and can be understood by analysing which action plans resulted in the highest pay offs. In general, American and European manufacturers have benefited from structural changes in manufacturing: reorganising the manufacturing function, redeploying workers, and linking manufacturing more closely to strategy. The Japanese, on the other hand, seem to find the most benefit from fundamental process development, quality function deployment and quality circles.

Training of workers, supervisors, and managers has paid off handsomely everywhere. It was ranked at the top of the list for the Europeans, and in the top tier for the Americans and Japanese. For the Americans, the investments in statistical process control and just-in-time programmes are starting to show results. The Japanese continue to benefit from quality circles (but, interestingly, not the Europeans) and from the constant search for new production processes for both old and new products.

By comparing the lists from the 1990 survey with those of previous surveys, there is at least one relatively new item on each of the three. In the American list, it is interfunctional work teams. The resulting shorter lines of communications, reduced bureaucracy, freer flow of information, mutual trust, and other benefits from this approach are proving worthwhile. On the European list, the new item is quality function deployment (QFD): a set of techniques for determining and communicating customer needs and translating them into product and service design specifications and manufacturing methods. QFD is also on the Japanese list of high-pay-off programmes.

For the Japanese, the new item on the list is computer-aided design (CAD). It is interesting that CAD has started to pay off, while other computerisation programmes such as computer-aided manufacturing (CAM), integration of information systems between manufacturing and other functions, and even flexible manufacturing systems (FMS) have not had a good pay off at all. The focus on CAD is symptomatic of the Japanese intent to create the design factory of the future.

The most interesting result of the analysis is not the definition of the value-adding, the boundary-free or the design factory of the future. The important result is that, in contrast to what is sometimes suggested in the business press, there is not one, but many conceivable factories of the future. Each represents, in its region, a viable option for competitors in the short or medium term. The challenge for each manufacturing or general manager is to identify the direction in which a factory should evolve.

In this process alternatives arise. Some of them will come from within a company, others will be created by competitors. In both cases, the speed with which new programmes and manufacturing concepts are implemented will be important. If it is a company idea, it will be copied, and reaping the benefits of creativity requires staying ahead of imitators. If it is a competitor's idea, the gap needs to be closed as quickly as possible.

How do companies speed up implementation? Four guidelines can be suggested: continuous experimentation, implementing small but continuous improvements, empowering production managers and creating a clear vision.

THE NEED FOR CONTINUOUS EXPERIMENTATION

As mentioned in Chapter 6, a series of improvement programmes have been introduced over the past two decades. After discovering statistical process control, there was the implementation of quality circles, flexibility in qualitative growth, just-in-time delivery systems, value analysis, computer integrated manufacturing, customer based manufacturing, time based competition, lean manufacturing, etc.

These programmes have one thing in common: none of them were conceived of by academics. They were all introduced by leading companies. It is a sobering thought for the academic world. But perhaps it would be impossible to design this type of programme behind a desk, through formal analysis. Most of these programmes have grown organically. They never followed a clear path. While envying Toyota's kanban systems, we should remember that the system is the result of years of experimentation.

So here lies the dilemma. Before implementing a programme, should a company wait for a competitor to create and test it, or should it try to lead the way? Leading is better, even if it is only in a limited area. But if that is the objective, the slack required for experimentation must be created. This means establishing some surplus capacity in manufacturing. This does not mean becoming inefficient. But if we need a given capacity to meet the demand, companies could add an additional 10 per cent in slack capacity to allow for experimentation and pilot projects. This does not imply spreading demand of 100 over a production capacity of 110. Factories should be run as efficiently as possible, but have the capacity to carry out trial runs.

In a company with several factories, capacity for experimentation could be concentrated in a few leading factories, which become centres of production excellence. But the principle remains. To cumulative capacity a surplus for experimentation is added. If production leadership is concentrated in a few factories, methods must be designed for diffusing results to other factories.

Furthermore, experiments entail both successes and failures – probably more failures than successes. Only when experimentation systems have been created with the appropriate tools for a postmortem analysis of both successes and failures can it be considered a learning production organisation that provides leadership in the development of new production improvement programmes. Such an approach may sound inefficient in the short-term, but is absolutely necessary for the long-term development of learning capabilities needed for quick implementation of new programmes.

CONTINUOUS IMPROVEMENT METHODS

In order to create improvements one can theoretically follow two paths: small steps and small improvements, or big steps, break-through type projects (Figure 9.1).

Both approaches should lead to a similar result over time. Yet the practice seems to be different. Although big step improvements seem theoretically feasible, in reality they are impossible to realise overnight. It requires time to overcome teething problems and debug the system.

Big step improvements

I was once involved in the start up of a major greenfield site petrochemical plant. That is obviously a major step. The first time that the plant was 'switched on', it ran for a fraction of a second. With much hard work, energy and dedication, the engineers and the workforce succeeded after about six months in reaching 99 per cent capacity utilisation. But once the start-up period was over, dedication and energy went back to normal levels and capacity utilisation slipped slightly. Performance improvement evolved following the graph in Figure 9.2.

Performance slips because of a slide in dedication and energy, but perhaps also because the best engineers are already looking

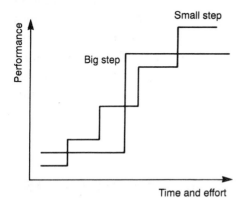

Figure 9.1 How to obtain performance improvements?

forward to the next big project. In companies with performance improvement cultures based on big steps, there is no glory to be gained from smaller improvements or maintenance. A similar phenomenon can be observed in the development of large software projects. Immediately after installing the software, there is a lot of effort that goes into the debugging. But once the system runs more or less acceptably, no one is really interested in updating or maintaining it. The real fun is with the new big project.

Small step improvements

Does this mean that a continuous improvement approach, one that implements improvement in small steps, is more certain and less risky? This approach can lead to better overall performance, but there are two major risks (Figure 9.3).

The first one is that one small improvement cancels out the previous one. Quality improvements due to a change in raw materials may ultimately have a negative impact on the quality of the product because a machine has problems in processing the new material. To avoid this, a clear vision is important, as a light beacon guiding each small step.

It is somewhat simplistic, but companies should apply a short list of questions and checkpoints to any proposal development. In the

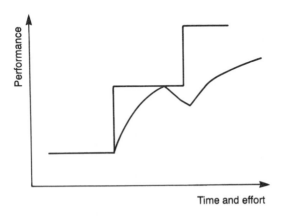

Figure 9.2 The reality of big step improvements

figure, this is suggested by drawing a 'tunnel' around a sequence of small steps. The tunnel 'guides' the development. Within the tunnel, steps can vary in size, small contradictions can be accepted, but the tunnel forces every improvement to contribute to achieving the final objective.

The second risk of small step improvement is the decreasing marginal returns of small improvements (Figure 9.3).

Due to the reduced potential improvement in productivity, for a given level of investment, every step begins to have a smaller impact. That may be because the process technology potential has been exhausted, or because greater sophistication is required which goes beyond the knowledge level of employees. In such cases, it may be necessary to take one big step (Figure 9.4). A totally new factory may have to be built, based on new technological concepts.

The telecommunications industry offers an example. About ten years ago, a telephone switch was essentially an electronic product with a very high hardware content. Factories of telephone exchanges were basically assembly lines of electronic products. Improving such a line involved streamlining the flow of the products, automating component insertion and assembly tasks, and speeding up some of the steps.

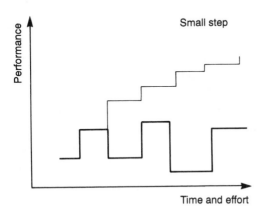

Figure 9.3 Risks of small step improvements

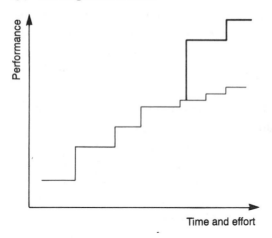

Figure 9.4 Alternating small steps with one big step

A telephone switch is still an electronic product, but the software content has become dominant. A major part of production has become installation, testing and debugging. While hardware production was the main value adding activity a decade ago, telecommunications companies are increasingly emphasising software production. The same is true for more mundane electronic products. Today's television set is almost all hardware with some electronic components. Five years from now, television sets will be about 50 per cent software. That means that companies like Philips and Thomson have to turn completely around. So much change is difficult to achieve through a series of small steps.

The transition from one type of product to another requires a big step. It cannot be avoided. But company management should be aware that big steps, in a culture dominated by continuous improvements, requires a very different project management approach. It has to be managed outside the traditional structures of the company with the attention of top management and careful risk management.

If dealing with these two issues is possible, small, continuous improvements have a high potential of achieving performance improvements quickly. They also create an additional advantage. The more often one implements a change, the better one becomes at doing it. By applying the small step approach, a company creates the potential for continuous change, and learns how to implement it.

THE NEW MANUFACTURING ORGANISATION

The new manufacturing organisation is an organisation which understands that new concepts in manufacturing are not available on the shelf of some kind of manufacturing candy store. New concepts develop through experimentation. Success depends less on developing and recognising new concepts, than it does on being faster than the competition in implementing them.

Speed, in turn, requires an organisation with production managers who are empowered production entrepreneurs, attracted enough by the company's manufacturing vision to orient their experiments in a similar direction, and to quickly share the results with the rest of the organisation. The manufacturing staff's role in such an organisation is no longer the learning and development of new manufacturing processes off-line. Instead, it must stimulate production entrepreneurs to carry out on-line experiments, provide support to increase the value of the experimentation, and facilitate the diffusion of knowledge throughout the company.

EMPOWERING PRODUCTION MANAGERS

Lots of experimentation, many small step improvements and an organisation that is used to change hardly sounds like a traditional manufacturing organisation. The caricature of manufacturing organisations is one of strict schedules, static and hierarchical structures, lots of bureaucratic rules and procedures, and an unwillingness to co-operate with design and marketing. Such an organisation is not likely to create a culture for the speedy implementation of new manufacturing programmes.

Success depends on pushing responsibility for experimentation and implementation down to the lowest supervisory levels in the organisation, and by directly involving employees in the design and implementation of performance improvement plans. That is hardly standard practice. Production improvements tend to follow hierarchical lines, are often under strict scrutiny by financial control staff, and changes are limited to areas where they would have the least disruptive effect on output.

This is not a recommendation to do away with all of these controls. Sound evaluation, justification of major investments, and solid risk management are good manufacturing practice. But in order to speed up implementation, manufacturing managers must release the creativity and drive for experimentation that exist lower down in the hierarchy. Plant managers or workshop supervisors should be empowered so that they develop into some kind of internal production entrepreneurs. They must have both the incentive to experiment and the freedom to allocate resources. Implementing new ideas and testing new concepts should be done on a decentralised basis.

STRONG VISION

A host of entrepreneurial, empowered production managers, each carrying out production experiments in their corner, could lead to chaos. Each individual experiment may be of interest, but they may add up to nothing for the company if they point in different directions or if the results are not communicated throughout the organisation. Figure 9.5, a picture of a set of steel nails, describes the situation. The nails represent the action of individual production managers. If there is no guide, and the nails are thrown randomly, they will point in different directions.

In order to establish some structure, a magnet is needed to point all the nails in more or less the same direction. The magnet symbolises the manufacturing manager's vision, as well as the communication mechanisms which quickly diffuse the results of the experiments. The magnet also has another meaning. A magnet 'seduces' the nails to point in a particular direction, it does not impose structure by force. The vision exerted by manufacturing managers is not the list of executive orders which used to trickle down the hierarchical structure of a traditional manufacturing organisation.

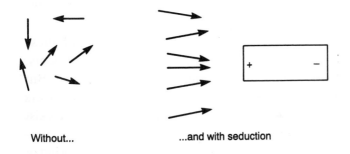

Without...   ...and with seduction

Figure 9.5 Guiding production managers

SUMMARY

Continuous Experimentation
Capacity for experimentation must be added to cumulative capacity. This is the root of innovation – both the successes and the failures.

Continuous Improvement
Two principal methods exist for implementing manufacturing improvements:
- big step improvements
- small step improvements.

It is possible to alternate several small step improvements with one big step.

New Manufacturing Organisations
Production managers need to be empowered and become entrepreneurs within the limits and context of the manufacturing vision, to experiment and improve continuously.

10 PERFORMANCE MEASUREMENT

Defining new battlegrounds in manufacturing and implementing the related performance improvement programmes requires a new approach to performance measurement. Companies have long relied on cost accounts to assess operational performance. The classic double-entry accounts of costs, revenues, assets and liabilities were considered *the* comprehensive database of cause and effect relationships determining the financial outcome of operating activities. Over the past decade, however, there has been growing criticism of this reliance on accounting in managing world class operations.

This chapter looks at some of the criticisms of current performance measurement systems and suggests some alternative solutions.

WHY THE DISSATISFACTION?

Much of current management accounting practice dates back to the beginning of this century. It typically focuses heavily on costs and ignores other measures which might reflect quality, flexibility or dependability priorities. There is no secret about why these other dimensions were neglected. Cost efficiency was a key element of competitiveness until the middle of the 1970s. It had the advantage of being measured in monetary terms, a language easily understood by a company's shareholders and partners. Everyone from accountants and marketing colleagues to shareholders and equipment vendors understood what a dollar was.

Not all of them share a similarly homogeneous understanding of 'quality defects' measured as parts per million, or of the importance of the 'percentage of on-time deliveries'. Yet in a world where competition is not even mainly based on prices and the entailing cost pressures, and where other missions in manufacturing may play a dominant supporting role in obtaining a customer's order, we need to include more physical and operational measurements: ppm defect rates, first pass yields, scrap, obsolescence, product varieties, throughput measures and delivery performance measures. Cost accounting systems are no longer sufficient for measuring performance.

These systems focus on direct labour. Fixed costs are allocated on the basis of how direct labour is used in producing different products or processes. That would be an acceptable practice, if direct labour represented the company's major direct cost. In practice, direct labour has become a relatively unimportant factor of production. Focusing on materials utilisation might have instilled very different management practices. Instead of relentlessly pursuing labour productivity, the result might have been more attention paid to materials utilisation, which could have led to a realisation of the enormous burden of scrap, rework, etc., at an earlier stage of industrial development.

Current cost accounting systems could be adapted to respond to these objections, but they have more trouble dealing with the challenge of integration. The key concept of this book is the need to develop an integrated view of the value creation process. Standard cost accounting practices tend to optimise costs in a given unit. But in order to offer customers top value, companies must optimise the combined performance of suppliers, designers, manufacturers, assemblers, distributors and dealers. It is not the cost or the quality of a system component which interests customers, but the package of product and service.

Optimising each and every component of a product does not necessarily lead to an optimal end product. Computer suppliers who assemble mainframes, input/output systems and sets of communication devices, have found out the hard way that if every sub-supplier optimises their production and delivery system, product components no longer arrive at the same time at the customer's location. Customers are not really interested in receiving wonderful CPUs if they have to wait several more weeks for the terminals and printers.

Another difficulty of current practice is the inability to measure learning. Previous chapters have stressed that a static view of manufacturing does not make sense. The manufacturing organisation of the future is one that learns continuously, and strains to improve daily. Static measurements of costs, quality, delivery performance and flexibility are useful, but do not provide the impetus for the model to change. Knowing the resources used to produce a product is important, but so is learning how to use resources more effectively. Kaplan, Harvard Business School's well known accounting specialist, summarised manufacturing managers' training regarding cost accounting systems for performance measurement as follows:

> 'The traditional measures produced irrelevant or misleading information, at worst, provoked behaviour that undermined the achievement of strategic objectives. Measures that tracked each dimension of performance in isolation were destroying management's understanding of how effectively the organization as a whole was implementing the company's strategy. Traditional performance measures did not take into account the requirements and perspectives of the customers, both internal and external. Bottom-line financial measures come too late (monthly) for mid course corrections and remedial actions.'[1]

Furthermore, the internationalisation of manufacturing will lead to the creation of networks of plants. One of the objectives of a good performance measurement system is to enable manufacturing managers to understand the strengths and the weaknesses of their networks. Plants operate in environments which differ from each other due to external influences such as geographical conditions, labour relations, raw material supply, costs of capital and government regulations, as well as the company's choice of mission for the plant. It becomes almost impossible to design a

---

[1] Kaplan R.S., 1990, *Measures for Manufacturing Excellence*, Harvard Business School Press, Boston.

performance measurement system that draws an objective comparison of all a company's plants. Yet this is necessary to allow shifts in production among existing factories, to evaluate investments in new production capacities or to close plants.

MEASURING ACTIVITIES RATHER THAN COSTS

Today's financial measurement systems need not be done away with, but should serve as a complement to direct operational measures. For manufacturing managers, direct and operational measurements of physical parameters are far more relevant than monthly financial statements. Manufacturing costs are the consequence, not the source, of activities. To reduce costs, activities that create costs and value for the customer should be measured, so that improvements can be made directly to the underlying activities. If quality, dependability and responsiveness can be improved, automatic improvements in costs are obtainable, as demonstrated in Chapter 8.

In terms of measurement, that implies that financial summaries should be the result of underlying activities. This is contrary to current approaches where financial statements come first and operating managers are then required to come up with operational explanations of what went wrong. It seems that the current accounting systems put the cart before the horse. Costs do not drive activities, activities drive costs.

Johnson[2] described how General Electric (US) implemented an activity-based system in its plants. The whole system was based on the premise that a competitive business must provide value to customers at a cost lower than the sales price. Activities carried out in the plants can consume resources either to create that value (such as quality) for the customer, or they can lead to waste (such as rework). Performance measurement systems must aim at reducing waste producing activities and improve resource

---

[2] Johnson H.T., 1990, *Performance Measurement for Competitive Excellence*, Kaplan R., 1990, op. cit.

deployment for value creation.

A good performance measurement system, therefore, should push companies to redesign their measurement system to monitor the complete value chain – adding such activities as design of product specifications or final customer payments. Obviously, this leads the company to focus on any activity that might cause delay in delivery or variations in capacity utilisation.

In order to introduce such a system, GE recognised that it needed information on all the activities carried out in the company. It then needed to identify which created value and which created waste. It sounds straightforward. Assembling a product creates value, doing rework is a waste. But many activities are more difficult to classify. Is implementing an engineering change order value creation or waste? If it improves the product by responding better to customer needs it creates value. But if engineering has to change because of a design error, it becomes waste. Yet in practice many engineering change roles would combine a real improvement with the repair of a design fault. Similarly, is employee communication a waste or does it create value? And what about on-the-job training?

Value creation is often strongly linked to waste activities. A large amount of work-in-process is often due to the unreliability of machines. If machines break down regularly, manufacturing personnel will tend to buffer them with 'buffer stocks' to avoid production line disruptions. Management of this work-in-process is obviously a waste of activity. But customers do care about on-time delivery, and waste activity supports the value creation. The cause of the waste is the unreliable machinery, but it may not be always that easy to eliminate the cause of the waste activity. Worse, we know that quality problems often have multiple causes. It may not always be as straightforward as in the example of the unreliable machine. Work-in-process may be due to mistakes in procurement, sloppiness in production planning and control or an inefficient factory layout. Eliminating the waste activity completely may become a daunting task in such a situation.

The situation is not always as fuzzy and difficult as the one described above. In many cases, a simple ABC analysis is possible:

clarify the main waste activities and their sources, measure them, and then tackle their improvement. GE used this type of analysis to identify two of the most frequent causes of waste: defective parts from vendors and poor process layout. Both contributed to the five major waste activities:

- accumulating materials;
- expediting;
- moving;
- testing; and
- reworking.

Both the causes and the five waste activities are easily measurable in non-monetary terms. Focusing measurement on these causes and activities allowed GE to revise and improve factory layout and pushed staff to contact and work with vendors on quality problems.

The improvements obtained over a period of nine months were impressive: product lead time cut by 60 per cent, final testing defects by 50 per cent, total payable costs by 21 per cent, work-in-process by 50 per cent, stock-room transactions by 57 per cent, and the number of on-time deliveries increased by 5 per cent.

The logic of performance measurement and evaluation based on an analysis of underlying activities, rather than on superficial cost consequences, is easy to accept. But here again implementation is the key. In the 1990 Manufacturing Futures Survey, many respondents expressed interest in 'activity-based cost accounting systems', but it turned out to be one of the programmes with the lowest payoffs. This is due to implementation problems.

By 1990, several companies had started experimenting with activity-based accounting systems, but these experiments had not yet yielded meaningful results. The hurdles to overcome are huge. Managing by cost has been a management credo for years. Capital markets and investors ultimately judge a company by its bottom line. But the more managers and shareholders increase their understanding of the fact that long-term profitability results from being competitive, not from juggling accounting numbers, the easier it will become to complement activity-based measurements with financial statements.

A MORE SYSTEMATIC VIEW OF COSTS – TOTAL COST OF OWNERSHIP

Competitiveness in the market is not simply the result of the company's value creating activities. Supplied components and sub-assemblies incorporated into the final product play an equally important role in customer satisfaction. Company performance needs to be evaluated, but measures must reflect how the whole value creating system performs.

The role of procurement is extremely important in the relationship with suppliers and the total value creation process. In measuring the performance of a procurement department one will want to de-emphasise a purchase price variance measure. Yet purchasing costs are an important variable for decision making if they can be combined with other attributes. This has led some companies to evaluate vendors and purchasing departments not merely by the purchase price but by what they have called *'total cost of ownership'*.

In addition to the purchase price of components and sub-assemblies, cost of ownership includes a whole set of associated costs – ordering and paying, scheduling, receiving, inspecting, handling deliveries, materials storage, scrap and rework of items of unsatisfactory quality, obsolescence of materials and costs of disruption due to incorrect delivery.

This may, in the short term, lead to a higher purchasing unit price, but offer perspectives in the long term for a much more effective and cheaper delivery process, where a number of the transactions (inspection, rework etc.) may be omitted, or strongly reduced. Texas Instruments has strongly emphasised this idea of total cost of ownership in its relationships with its customers for semiconductor devices. Based on their intention to build strategic partnerships with their customers, they have developed a methodology whereby suppliers and customers work together on all aspects of quality, design and service. The methodology embraces the full life cycle of products: from conception, design and testing through to procurement, manufacture and service.

The methodology provides a basis which helps the partner

involved to understand every activity in the relationship in terms of its cost. How much does it really cost to hold an unnecessary inventory or to accept long suppliers lead times? What do we spend on all the paperwork and information systems which are needed to manage the relationship with a supplier? How much does one spend on testing of outgoing materials at the supplier's site and the incoming materials at the customer's site? How much do we loose in margins if a product is late? How much do we pay for insurance against warranty claims?

Texas Instruments argues that by applying this methodology in collaboration with customers such as Sony, Italtel, Siemens-Nixdorf, Alcatel or Ericsson they have been able to spot and eliminate hidden costs, streamline quality and testability into product design, manage customer inventory needs and implement state-of-the-art processes to minimise cost and time-to-market. An example may help to understand this.

The cost of testing electronics is rising at the same speed as the device and system complexity of the end product. When you consider the cost for fault detection, fault isolation and fault elimination/repair, up to 25 per cent of a product's total life cycle cost is spent on testing. This includes incoming inspection of chips, laboratory analysis of a prototype board, outgoing manufacturing test of a system, and diagnosis of a malfunctioning unit in the field. Furthermore, the typical cost of repairing a fault increases by a factor of ten as a design evolves from a device by itself, to a component on a board, or two boards within a system. Test engineers have become increasingly alarmed by these cost escalations.

Until now organisational separations prevented companies from finding system-wide solutions. But in the electronics industry a solution seems to be around the corner. Its aim is to move testing and manufacturing considerations up to the first steps in the design cycle.

Alcatel's Belgian subsidiary has done a study of components with or without a 'boundary scan'. This is a method that requires that circuitry be added to the device specifically for test purposes. The scanning allows test instructions and data to be serially loaded in the system and to be read out serially. This simplifies the task of isolating faults, as well as finding short and open circuits due to flawed interconnections, missing components and other problems. Alcatel found in a cost-benefit analysis that significantly less money was spent in fault detection and isolation, rework and rejects on testing equipment, when boards incorporated boundary scan capabilities. Engineering costs were reduced to about 85 per cent of the costs for boards and production test related costs varied between 70 and 90 per cent of the costs for the normal boards. Such benefits can, however, only be realised when supplier and customer work together on the circuit design and have a common 'cost of ownership' approach to realise the advantages.

Developing a cost-of-ownership measure is quite similar to computing a cost of quality. Both the cost of ownership and cost of quality attempt to provide an overall financial summary, cutting across all organisational boundaries, of all expenses associated with two important activities: purchasing materials and elementary defects. In that sense, cost of ownership is a particular application of activity based performance measurement, with the specific characteristic that it transcends the organisation. If this is possible for total quality and total cost of ownership, we may start thinking creatively about what else would be conceivable: total cost of design? total cost of delivery? There are many variations possible and the task for the senior manufacturing manager consists of finding the 'total cost of . . .' which best fits the manufacturing mission of the organisation.

PERFORMANCE MEASUREMENT FOR LEARNING

Companies need not only to keep quality, delivery or mix of products under control. They also need to improve on these items. Constant improvement and innovation is necessary in order to stay ahead of the competition. After European customers got a taste of what was possible with Japanese style JIT systems, pressure has mounted everywhere to install these systems and to improve performance. Total quality control requires a steady level of improvement in error reduction and service delivery. But what is the correct level of improvement? And what are the targets to go for? Stata, the chairman of US based Analog Devices[3] says he has learned that there is a rational basis on which to set standards for rates of improvement. He has a set of documented cases which indicate that while the rate of improvement varies from case to case, the rate in each case is remarkably consistent over an extended time period. An improvement of, for example 50 per cent in number of defects was obtained in a remarkably stable period for each case. As for nuclear decay he called this characteristic slope of improvement, or decay of defect level the half life time. An analysis of a relatively large number of cases revealed that the half life time for improvement fell within a relatively narrow range, something in between six to 12 months across a wide range of applications.

The reason for that is perhaps simple. Companies use a fairly standardised approach to problem solving in manufacturing. They identify and prioritise the causes of the problems, assign a team to solve the problems and eliminate the causes. In many cases the cycle of improvement is largely a function of the complexity and the bureaucracy of the organisation, and surprisingly not very related to the skills of the people or the level of resources. These do have an impact, but organisational factors play an equally important, if not more important role.

Such a half life concept can be used to set more aggressive goals for improvement. After a careful analysis of the past experience in organisational learning and improvement, one can set slightly more challenging objectives. The results can be awesome. If the organisation would have a half life of, for example, the defect level of outgoing products of about 12 months, the resulting improvement after five years leads to a defect rate of 3.125 per cent of the original level. If we reduce the half life time to 6 months we reach a level of 0.0098 per cent. The difference may not be that big at first sight, but it is perhaps the difference between a constantly lower performance than your competition, or a consistently better

[3] Stata R., 1989, Organisational Learning, The Key to Management Innovation, *Sloan Management Review*, Spring, pp. 63–73.

performance. Both improvement levels are realistic. It illustrates the difference between a company that does continuous improvements and a company that aggressively focuses the reduction of its half life time of improvements.

MEASURING AT AN INTERNATIONAL OR MULTIDIVISIONAL LEVEL

A supplementary degree of complication in performance measurement is how to compare plants which are more or less similar. Often people believe that an objective performance comparison is eventually impossible. They would argue that the environment and characteristics of plants are so diverse that comparison exercises become irrelevant. These characteristics include local conditions, such as industrial relations or government regulations, the age of the plant equipment, the size of the plant which influences the degree to which one can obtain economies of scale or could fall into diseconomies of scale, the characteristics of the workforce, the degree of competition in the region served by the plant etc. Yet even if one takes into account all these factors, a residual difference in productivity remains.

Chew, et al[4] have studied the total productivity of more than 40 operating units of an industrial kitchen company that prepare, deliver and serve up food. After controlling at the output side for some minor differences in menus prepared, and filtering out all the variation due to the variety of external forces that may create the tremendous variation in productivity, they still found a residual variation of about 2 to 1 between the 40 odd plants. They explain the persistence of the sizeable differences by the degree to which the managers of these units have grasped the opportunity to improve on the performance. Interplant performance measurement should first and foremost attempt to reveal these differences in improvement, the ideas that can be transferred to other sites. Secondly the performance measurements should

---

[4] Chew W.B., Bresnaham T.F. and Clark K.B., 1990, Measurement, Co-ordination and Learning in a Multiplant Network, in Kaplan R.S., op. cit.

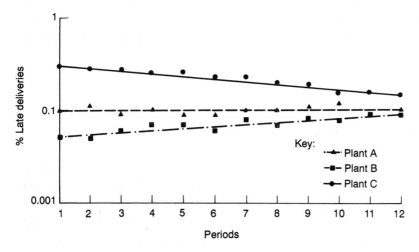

Figure 10.1 Delivery performance – an example

also provide the incentives to do the transfer of the learning across the plants in the different geographical locations. The company should reward plant managers not only for the contribution they make to the management of their own plant, but also for the advances they realise for the firm as a whole. A score card based on the half life time to obtain improvements can also be used for the international comparison of different plants. In Figure 10.1 we have provided a theoretical example with three plants. Assume that we are interested in measuring the delivery performance of a plant, measured as the percent of late deliveries. This percentage is measured over a period of 12 months and plotted on a log-linear scale versus time. Plant A has a relatively stable performance: over the last 12 periods, it has delivered about 10 per cent of its products late. Plant B has a better performance of 5 per cent late deliveries by the beginning of the period but seems to deteriorate slightly. Plant C starts out very badly with 30 per cent late deliveries and has by the end of the period still a performance worse than the other plants (15 per cent). Which is the best plant? From an absolute performance level, it is plant B. But plant C, though still worse than plant A and B, has a much shorter half life time of improvements and may well catch up very quickly with the other plants and overtake them in performance. Perhaps structural factors such as new equipment or bad local political conditions created the low initial performance. But the plant manager of plant C seems to have found a way of gradually getting the plant up to world standards.

The example shows that performance comparison at an absolute level may not be appropriate. Comparison of half life times may create a healthy competition to generate the fastest improvement curve. It becomes obvious and embarrassing when one does not perform well. In another company I have observed a similar system of comparisons on the basis of improvement. Apart from a total cost curve, which displayed falling costs from month to month, I saw as well a number of related graphs on process times, number of defects, changeover times, number of line stops, inventory levels, etc. Each of these curves emphasised the proportional level of improvement as opposed to the absolute level at one point in time. And as an interesting aside, it is worth mentioning that all of these indicators went upwards. The scales were adapted in such a way that the evolution of costs or defects created a positive reinforcement upwards. Only the sky is the limit for this company's plants. This example suggests another important lesson. The company was very careful not to use one single measure or set of measures to evaluate its plants. With different missions or plant charters it had to use different measurements of performance improvements. Though all measures were displayed for all plants, the comparisons were made only in so far they were related to a plant's mission.

The pattern that emerges from these examples and studies may provide us with a framework for interplant comparison. First of all, as we argued in Chapter 7, plants should have clearly stated missions and charters which explain these missions, and against which performance can be measured. Secondly, though we should not set aside absolute measures to see to what extent a plant lives up to its original mission, we are probably better off in using comparisons of performance improvements between plants, in order to account for the differences created by local conditions and idiosyncratic plant characteristics. Thirdly, this performance improvement comparison should stimulate healthy intra-plant competition, but not one that would inhibit transfer of innovative practices between plants. Performance evaluation of managers has to include their individual plant's performance as well as how they enhance the performance of the firm as a whole. Finding the appropriate balance between incentives favouring the plant's and the company's performance will be a delicate exercise which must both create enough incentives for local learning and entrepreneurial initiative as well as the improvement of communications between the plants.

SUMMARY

Performance Measurement
Dissatisfaction with current manufacturing performance measurement systems is due to the fact that they focus too much on costs and disregard current missions. Cost accounting systems are no longer enough to measure manufacturing performance
- activities must be measured, rather than costs
- the 'total cost of ownership' reflects the entire value creating chain.

Developing such an approach is similar to computing a cost of quality.

The notion of half life is the characteristic slope of improvement, or decay of defect level was developed by Analog Devices. This approach can be used to introduce aggressive improvement goals.

International Measurement
- the half life concept is also useful internationally because performance comparisons at an absolute level may not be appropriate
- comparing half lives generates healthy competition for the fastest improvement curves.

11 A GENERAL MANAGEMENT VIEW OF MANUFACTURING

This summary is not a manual of how to apply the different concepts discussed in the book, but rather a road map for the general manager who wants to review the role of the manufacturing function.

MAKING MANUFACTURING EXTERNALLY SUPPORTIVE

Manufacturing can play an important role in creating sustainable competitive advantage. To do so, the old view of manufacturing, as a neutral function in the company, must be shed. Manufacturing management is no longer about neutralising the potentially negative effects of the production process.

Today, manufacturing should aim to support business strategy, or even to be one of the key pillars on which it rests. This radical shift requires companies to define productivity in a new way. Traditionally, output volume was related to the total sum of production factors used by manufacturing. But manufacturing output also means satisfying customers with an appropriate portfolio of goods and services. Input is the intelligent deployment of production resources, integrating the fact that direct labour has become a virtually marginal cost in the production process, where capital equipment and material are dominant. This approach to productivity requires careful choices about how to satisfy customers and how to increase the efficiency of capital equipment and materials use.

To satisfy customers, a company can pursue different options, or combinations of manufacturing missions. We distinguished five major types of manufacturing mission:

- cost efficiency;
- quality;
- flexibility in design;
- flexibility in volume; and
- delivery reliability.

Companies dream of beating their competitors in all of these areas but that is impossible given current technological and other constraints. Companies have to make choices: which mission to pursue to excel and win orders, and which to classify 'good enough' to qualify for competition.

This choice is one that should not be left to operational managers. They may inadvertently impose constraints on a company's strategic freedom of movement by investing in a particular technology or production system. The choice should rest with a senior manager, and it is a choice which must be made first and fast, because all other decisions in manufacturing depend on it.

Plastivaloire is a medium sized French company that produces plastic parts by injection moulding. It exemplifies this approach. One of Plastivaloire's major customers is Philips consumer electronics. Each day, the Philips factory in Dreux needs between 1,000 and 1,500 chassis for television sets, equipped with certain components such as loudspeakers or certain push buttons. Philips insisted that its suppliers deliver just in time and made clear that it would be draconian about quality. For Plastivaloire, the message was clear: a combination of quality and delivery reliability had to lie at the core of its manufacturing mission.

To respond to the challenge, it built a dedicated plant a few hundred metres from the Philips factory. To improve communication and collaboration between supplier and customer, it built a private road linking the two factories. The design of the factory, the decision to work in three shifts, and the relentless pursuit of a clean working environment contributed to ensuring customer satisfaction. The transport of products was automated to avoid using fork lift trucks that produce dust. The painting installation was pressurised and equipped with robots to ensure that the final touch was absolutely perfect. And the factory was a bit oversized to give an impression of space. That contributed to a feeling of well being for employees, and therefore to improved quality.

The example is simple, but illustrates that the company has thought through in detail how to best satisfy its customer, what that means for the definition of its manufacturing mission, and how to translate it into a coherent set of organisational factory decisions.

Defining a manufacturing mission is not an easy task. It requires a dynamic attitude because customers' needs change over time and manufacturing missions have to be re-evaluated accordingly. It can be helpful to use the mapping approach described in Chapter 3 to define current and future manufacturing missions.

TWO SPECIAL CASES: QUALITY AND FLEXIBILITY

Traditional manufacturing management was focused on cost efficiency. Frederick Taylor left an impressive and very successful legacy with his approach to scientific management. But today, companies have grown beyond that stage and other missions have become more important. This book paid particular attention to two of them: quality as a strategic tool, and cost efficient flexibility.

Quality is a concept which is often used and abused. Chapter 4 gave a short historic overview of quality management. It showed that our understanding of quality has evolved from an attitude which saw quality as a problem to be solved to one where quality is a strategic opportunity to be exploited. The idea is that an almost 'effortless' management of quality becomes the basis for a situation where we can create and introduce products propelled by a strong quality image, which, if well designed, will also delight the customer.

Manufacturing concepts of quality must be adapted to changing market requirements. This was illustrated by a simple model where manufacturing quality was represented by a square and customer requirements by a circle. An impossible challenge perhaps, but at least a clear target. How to manage that challenge deserves a book of its own. The key to success is to create a clear momentum for quality improvements. The categories used to award the US Baldridge Quality Award may be helpful for a comprehensive reflection of what operational levers create that momentum.

Cost efficient flexibility, or the ability to respond quickly to changing customer demands without yielding ground on costs is another fairly recent manufacturing mission. Flexibility has always been around. One could even argue that that was the area in which medieval corporations excelled. But being flexible and cost efficient at the same time requires very different production systems.

The major challenge posed by this type of flexibility is that it requires a systemic approach. A production system becomes more flexible, only if the entire value creation chain does – from supplies to deliveries. There is no reason for sub-optimisation of one part of the chain. The whole organisation and its external partners such as supplies or distributors, have to become flexible. A key interface in creating this flexibility is the one between design and manufacturing. Little time can be saved on the execution of technical tasks. Products and processes have to be developed, products have to be built. Time, however, can be saved in the transfer from design to products, and through the parallel solving of technical problems across different departments. Such parallel problem-solving creates new sets of interfaces, and increases the complexity of the interfacing process. Companies that want to combine flexibility with cost efficiency will have to become champions of interface management.

THE NEED FOR AN INTEGRATED APPROACH

The implementation of these two recent manufacturing missions can only be successful when the factory is integrated with other functions and with its external partners. Factories must live in symbiosis with their environment. That is not the way traditional factories were designed.

There are many good reasons which prevent a factory from cooperating with its partners. Some barriers are even the consequence of good management practice. Filters, for example, between market and factory are often the result of actions to simplify order processing. Barriers between manufacturing and suppliers are due to a search for cost reductions. The result is that factories tend to get isolated from their partners and can start to react counter-productively. The book argues for a gradual reduction of barriers between a factory and its supplier, employees, product and process design groups, customers, and the socio-economic environment in which the factory operates. It is not an easy task, because the reasons why barriers and buffers were created, often remain in place. Reducing barriers requires creative approaches to manage trade-offs between the need to reduce buffers and the cause of their existence.

Everybody is now convinced of the need to create solid partnerships between companies and suppliers, both for co-manufacturing and co-design. But that does not reduce the need to reduce costs, leading to hard-nosed discussion between a company and its suppliers. Cosy relationships only lead to complacency.

General Motors is a good example. Automobile industry studies have shown that excellent relationships with suppliers are an important element of competitive success. Yet the European operation of General Motors became successful by developing solid partnerships with extremely stringent cost optimisation programmes. Later on General Motors declared that it was looking for every opportunity to reduce its costs *worldwide*. It started a programme to save US$ 2 billion over three years. In the process, it wanted to help its suppliers identify areas of waste so that they too could lower their costs. Long standing, comfortable relationships between GM and its suppliers were to be replaced by more hard-headed criterion such as quality, price and service. GM also began to coordinate its purchasing on a global scale. US suppliers got the opportunity to sell overseas, while foreign suppliers compete with them in their home market.

This example leads to the second stage of the integration process. Factories must collaborate with other factories in the same group or company. That requires global management of factory networks. Successful factory network management depends on three things:

1. Defined charters for each factory which fit the overall manufacturing mission;
2. Performance measurement systems which recognise each factory's performance in fulfilling their manufacturing mission; and
3. The understanding that factory charters and associated performance measurement systems change over time.

The implementation of international networks requires extremely good communications. Xerox is an interesting example of a company that moved its manufacturing function from a collection of local manufacturing sites to an international network of integrated factories across the world. It began integrating globally in 1981 with purchasing materials and global sourcing, because that is where the company thought it could make the most money. In the process, it reduced the number of worldwide suppliers from more than 5,000 to just over 400. After the first successes, Xerox gradually adopted a global quality management programme, a new product delivery process, multinational taskforces for process design, a centralised logistics and asset management programme, and, by the end of the 80s, international product development teams.

Xerox's approach was a gradual one, based on a clear definition of a global manufacturing mission. It was followed by the creation of international capabilities, and good planning and prioritising to implement a global manufacturing strategy.

IMPLEMENTING LONG LASTING CHANGE

Manufacturing strategies are only useful if they are implemented, and if the results withstand the test of time. Chapter 8 described the intriguing fact that some companies were able to implement manufacturing improvements with a lasting impact, while others, after some initial success, seemed to lose momentum after a few months or years. How are lasting improvements in manufacturing created? A simple sand cone model was presented to illustrate that lasting improvements in manufacturing depends on two things:

- for capabilities to last, a certain sequence in their creation must be followed. First, quality capabilities, then dependability of production and delivery process, then reaction speed and finally, cost reduction
- these capabilities are cumulative and support each other. Investment in one of the more 'advanced' capabilities requires further investment in some of the earlier investments.

The central idea of this model is that for a company that is already operating efficiently, lasting cost improvements are a consequence of improvement actions, not a prerequisite for them.

The manufacturing organisation that becomes integrated while implementing lasting cost improvements will be unfamiliar territory. It will be driven by a very strong and attractive vision that adheres to the idea of continuous improvement and experimentation in the execution of its strategy. It will be managed by highly entrepreneurial production managers who have the creativity and the drive to give leadership to a programme of continuous experimentation. Plant managers and supervisors will have become production 'entrepreneurs' with the freedom to allocate resources and the incentive to experiment on a decentralised basis. The vision ensures that these production entrepreneurs do not run in different directions, but contribute to improving company performance.

Good measurement is an essential part of successful implementation. To ensure real and lasting performance improvements, measurement tools need to be adapted. Performance measurement should fulfill three criteria:

- it has to measure dynamic changes rather than the status quo. Measuring levels of inventories is not very exciting. Measuring changes in inventory rotation helps companies improve and learn
- it must measure physical elements close to the activities that take place in manufacturing; it is not useful to measure costs or monetary indicators far removed from the actual life of the production site, if the goal is to reduce defects and improve product quality
- performance measures should focus on activities that contribute to value creation for the customer. Excellent performance is not about doing things right, but about doing the right things. Performance measurements should help evaluate whether the right actions are being taken, and whether they improve customer satisfaction.

FROM REFLECTION TO ACTION

Just like war is too important to be left to the generals, manufacturing is too important to be left to technical specialists. Manufacturing does matter, today as much as it did 50 years ago. It is the cornerstone on which economic well-being is built. Survival in global competition will depend largely on how competitive the manufacturing function is. Preparing for competitiveness cannot be left to manufacturing specialists.

General managers have a very special role in stimulating strategic reflection concerning manufacturing. Manufacturing specialists can optimise and improve manufacturing plants, but general management is essential in ensuring manufacturing's cross-functional integration. This book sought to provide insights and tools for analysing the manufacturing function's potential contribution to the rest of the company and – more importantly – to the customer. Integrating with other functions is the key to customer-driven manufacturing. I hope that the reflection has been stimulating and invite you to start implementing some of the ideas presented in the book. Let's move from reflection to action. Let the customer drive manufacturing.

INDEX

Note: Page references to figures are followed by a letter 'f', e.g. '83f', those to tables by a letter 't', e.g. '39t', and those to footnotes by a letter 'n', e.g. '105n'.